To John
Best wishes

C000259938

The Royal Hospital Haslar

A Pictorial History

Aerial view looking towards the south-west in 1984.

THE
ROYAL HOSPITAL
HASLAR

A Pictorial History

*Eric Birbeck, Ann Ryder and
Phillip Ward*

PHILLIMORE

2009

Published by

PHILLIMORE & CO. LTD

Chichester, West Sussex, England

www.phillimore.co.uk

© Eric Birbeck, Ann Ryder, Phillip Ward, 2009

ISBN 978-1-86077-589-5

Printed and bound in Great Britain

CONTENTS

Preface

The closure of the Royal Hospital Haslar after nearly 256 years of continuous service to the Royal Navy, to all three services at times, and more recently to the National Health Service, is a significant event in the history of healthcare in Gosport, Portsmouth and southern Hampshire.

This book is not a history of the hospital; that has been achieved by a number of historians over the years. The Haslar Heritage Group has put together a pictorial record of the hospital, attempting to cover as many periods of time and locations within the hospital as possible. Thus, the book cannot hope to be a complete record and there will inevitably be areas that are not included. It is intended to stir fond memories in those who have served, lived and received treatment at Haslar.

Eric Birbeck
Ann Ryder
Phillip Ward
2009

In memoriam

Surgeon Vice Admiral Ian L. Jenkins CB CVO QHS FRCS RN

1944 - 2009

LIST OF ILLUSTRATIONS

Frontispiece: Aerial view looking towards the south-west in 1984

ACKNOWLEDGEMENTS

Illustration Acknowledgements

We would like to thank the following for permission to use their photographs:

The Scott Polar Research Institute, Cambridge for illustration 54.
The Imperial War Museum for illustrations 186 and 187.
The Late J.C. Lawrence, Photographer of Gosport, who donated illustrations 67 and 140 to Haslar.

The remaining illustrations are from organisations within and associated with the Defence Medical Services as follows:

The former Graphics, Media and Photography Department at Haslar, reproduced by kind permission of the Hospital Director Mrs Frances Allen.
Queen Alexandra's Royal Naval Nursing Service (QARNNS) and Voluntary Aid Detachment (VAD) archives held at the Institute of Naval Medicine, Alverstoke.
Members of the Haslar Heritage Group.

Other Acknowledgements

Quotations from 'A Visit to Haslar 1916' by Major General J. Richardson are reproduced by kind permission of the Medical Officer in Charge, The Institute of Naval Medicine, Alverstoke.
The 250th Anniversary Speech is reproduced by kind permission of Surgeon Captain R. Radford CBE, RN.
The Royal Hospital Haslar Closure Speech is reproduced by kind permission of Surgeon Captain J. Campbell FRCS(Ed), FRCS(En), RN.
The Haslar Heritage Group acknowledge, with grateful thanks, the assistance given by Captain Julia Massey RRC, QARNNS Archives, and Mrs Sylvia Bell, VAD Archives, in writing chapters and providing photographs.
Mr David Kirk's assistance in proof reading and helping the book reach publication.
The staff at Phillimore for their advice and patience.
Finally, the Haslar Heritage Group wish to acknowledge the support and encouragement given by friends and colleagues in the production of this book. Many of them are, like ourselves, serving or former members of the Defence Medical Services or civil servants associated with the recent history of the Royal Hospital Haslar. The responsibility for any errors or omissions, and for the views expressed in this book, is of course entirely our own.

INTRODUCTION

Before Haslar

Greenwich Hospital was established as a home for retired seamen, by charter of William and Mary in 1694, with pensioners accommodated there from 1705 until 1869. The serving sailor was less fortunate. Since 1660 ageing men-of-war, unfit for service, and hired merchant ships had been used as hospital ships. Overseas, sick-quarters were established in Jamaica in 1704, Lisbon in 1706 and Mahon, Minorca in 1708. Permanent purpose-built hospitals were constructed in Minorca in 1711, with construction at Port Royal, Jamaica and Gibraltar being authorised thirty years later in 1741.

At home, Admirals Drake and Hawkins had, in 1590, set up a medical fund for sick and injured sailors which became known as the Chatham Chest. During the Dutch Wars from 1652 to 1674, the number of injured resulted in four London hospitals being contracted to provide care for 'wounded and sick marryners'. The capacity to treat in London was inadequate. For the Portsmouth area, Portchester Castle was proposed as a site suitable for conversion to a hospital in 1653, but the 'old ruinous castle' was not used. Instead, private contractors received a shilling a day to treat patients in a variety of accommodation, some described as 'lurid ale-houses'.

In Gosport, the Fortune Hospital owned by Nathaniel Jackson near the present Lees Lane opened in 1713. It grew to 700 beds but seems to have had more emphasis on profit than quality of treatment. 'Violent and malignant fever' (Gaol fever or typhus)

1 *The Haslar peninsula was selected for the new hospital in 1745 with 95 acres of land being purchased the same year. At the time it was an isolated place with the harbour entrance to the north, the sea, shingle and Gilkicker point to the south and east, and to the west Blockhouse and Alverstoke Lakes. The site would be convenient for patients brought ashore from Spithead or to the hospital's jetty from Portsmouth Harbour.*

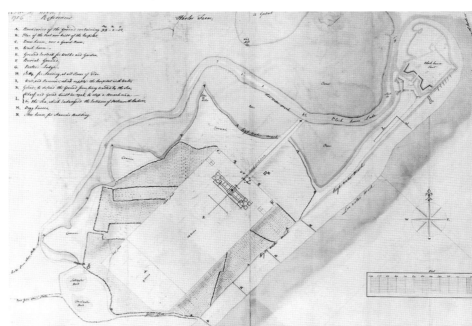

from 1739 to 1741 stretched the facilities ashore. In Gosport there were 'two or three in a bed' and such a stench that 'may breed the Plague'. Hospital ships were used in Portsmouth Harbour, the Commissioners for Sick and Wounded Seamen noting the significant reduction in drunkenness, gambling and desertion. 'Water was the prison wall' noted the Commissioners, and Portchester Castle was again considered as a place of confinement for naval patients in 1740 but suitable terms could not be agreed with the owners.

King George II was petitioned in 1741 'relating to the matter of the building of Naval Hospitals'. Overseas hospitals were approved but not those at home. Further complaints relating to the Forton or Fortune Hospital followed. The Earl of Sandwich, First Lord of the Admiralty, submitted a further memorial to the King in Council on 15 September 1744. While there was felt to be a need for hospitals in Portsmouth, Plymouth and Chatham, the Admiralty reduced the overall cost by asking only for a hospital at Portsmouth for £38,000 to house 1,500 patients. An order in Council accepted the memorial and, surprisingly, approved all three hospitals. Building started first in Plymouth but Haslar was completed and accepted patients first. Chatham was not built for some time.

2 *The hospital seen across Haslar Creek; Haslar jetty is to the left. Ships are at anchor at Spithead.*

3 *Haslar from Old Portsmouth, 1864. In the foreground is a shipyard in the Camber. On the right, across the harbour entrance, is Fort Blockhouse. On the left, the hospital appears isolated with none of today's clutter around it.*

Planning and Building Haslar

The Admiralty had clear ideas of the way they wished to see the hospital built, instructing the Commissioners of the Sick and Hurt Board that 'they would have the hospital to be strong, durable, plain building consisting of three stories; the same to form a large quadrangle with a spacious piazza within, the out fronts to be decent but not expensive'.

Sir Jacob Ackworth, the Surveyor of the Navy, was asked to produce a plan but also to consult with Theodore Jacobsen, a merchant and amateur architect who had recently designed the Foundling Hospital at Bloomsbury. Jacobsen was 'not entirely approving' of Ackworth's plan and promised 'to make one of his own which he believes may be better for the purpose'.

Jacobsen's plan, when finally produced, met with approval and was later published in the *Gentleman's Magazine*. The plan was for a double row of buildings joined at intervals but separated by a distance of about 35 feet. The architectural style is described as Palatial without ornamentation and was the forerunner of the Pavilion system of hospital design.

4 *Jacobsen's plan.*

5 *Theodore Jacobsen.*

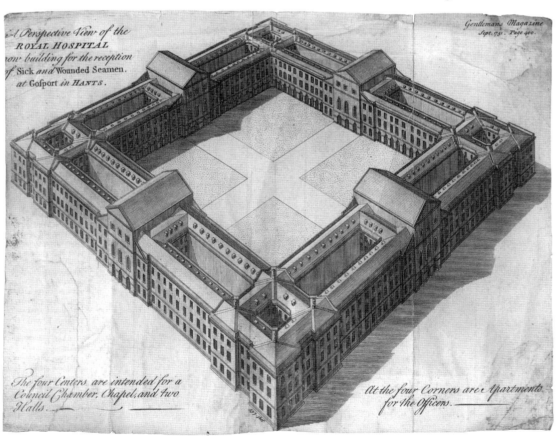

3

Foundations were laid in 1746 and Jacobsen's plan was executed by James Horne, a surveyor who had worked on the Foundling Hospital, and John Turner, a master carpenter from Portsmouth Dockyard.

Delays were caused by Press Gangs targeting carpenters, bricklayers and labourers building the hospital and by a storm that breached the sea wall towards Fort Blockhouse.

In 1749 the Earl of Sandwich, First Sea Lord, visited and noted that the front block was already built. He observed that the intended Council Chamber covering two floors in the centre was magnificent and directed that it should instead have an additional floor inserted and be converted to wards.

By 1751 the front blocks were nearly finished. Particular trouble was taken over the sewers with a report noting that 'these sewers communicate with every ward in the building and are dug so deep that the sea flowing in every tide, carries off all the soil at each ebb so that nothing of this kind could be contrived more necessary for health and sweetness'.

The pressure of numbers of potential patients forced the hospital to admit the first patients in October 1753.

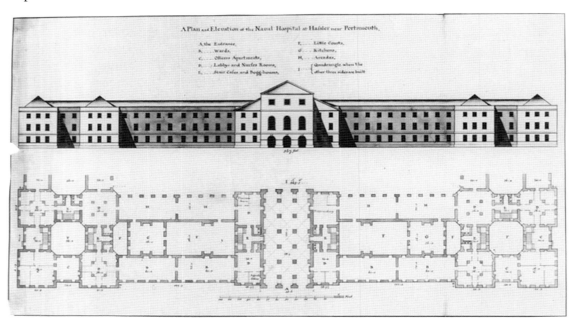

6   *Jacobsen's plan as executed by James Horne.*

THE LARGEST BRICK BUILDING

The front of the hospital is 567 feet long and is the only side to resemble the original plan. In 1758, while construction continued, James Lind wrote, 'Haslar Hospital is an immense pile of buildings ... it will certainly be the largest hospital in Europe when finished.' He estimated the final cost to be £100,000, some two and half times the original estimate, even though the fourth side was not built.

The hospital building occupied about seven acres with walls of immense thickness, decreasing from four feet thick at ground level to 18 inches in the attics.

7   *This picture is probably from the 1880s and is one of the earliest views of the front of the hospital. In the foreground, and behind some trees, Haslar Cottages can be seen. Haslar Cottages were used as the hospital washhouse from 1756 to 1876 and were subsequently used to house senior estate workers and their families. Behind the Cottages stand houses 11 and 12.*

8   *A Victorian view of the hospital and the main gate. The tram and narrow gauge rails indicate that this photograph was taken after 1877. It would have been the first view of the hospital for patients and visitors.*

9   *An aerial view of Haslar taken in the early 1960s. St Luke's Church has no roof and awaits rebuilding. Entry to the hospital is by the main gate at the bottom of the picture. The Zymotic (Infectious Diseases) blocks can be seen top left. On the lower edge is open ground that would soon be occupied by a new galley and Senior Rates Mess.*

6

10 *An Edwardian view of the centre block of the main façade shows the entrance to the Arcade through which patients passed to the receiving room. In this view the siding for the ambulance tram can be seen, with the main line passing through into the Arcade.*

11 *From the Arcade, St Luke's Church is seen across the quadrangle. This view was lost with the building of the new Crosslink complex in 1980.*

12 *An 1880s view of the main hospital façade. Many of the staff lived within the hospital and the Medical Mess is on the left of the picture. In the centre of the picture, at ground level, can be seen an entrance to the hospital cellars.*

13 *The pediment at the centre of the main façade contains a sculpture carved in Portland stone by Mr Thomas Pearce in 1752. In the centre of this sculpture are the Royal Arms of George II. On the left a female figure represents 'Navigation': she leans on a rudder and pours oil on the wounds of a sailor. Above her head shines the North Star, and a compass rests at her feet. Further out, in the angle, the left face of the sculpture is completed by the stem of a ship, with shells, pearls and zephyrs. On the right, 'Commerce' is seated among bales and chests, distributing money, fruit and flowers. Further out, a sailor in distress is being succoured by the serpent of Aesculapius carried in the beak of a bird. At the extreme angle of the right face is a group composed of Boreas, shells and ornaments.*

14 *Taken in 1976, this view of the hospital shows how car parking has changed the grounds. Trolleys stand in wait outside the receiving room. Emergency patients now enter through the door on the right of the picture. At this time the main operating theatres were on the first floor to the right, with the first floor between the theatres and the central arcade being occupied by the earliest intensive care unit.*

15 *An early 20th-century view of the front of the hospital.*

16 *During the Second World War blast walls were built along the ground floor allowing shelter and access to the cellars. Attic windows are still present.*

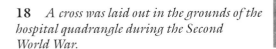

17 *A Second World War sign is still visible in 2009.*

18 *A cross was laid out in the grounds of the hospital quadrangle during the Second World War.*

19   *A fine view of the quadrangle taken from the cupola of St Luke's Church. It shows the large number of chimneys across the roofline of the hospital. On the first floor over the Arcade can be seen the canopy added to increase natural light to the newly opened first operating theatre. On the ground floor is the open colonnaded area that afforded shelter for patients and a covered walkway between the wards for staff in bad weather. For many years the right-hand covered area was used for mustering staff for the fortnightly pay parades.*

20   *A Victorian view of the hospital quadrangle, referred to as a piazza in the original description of the hospital. Staff and patients pose for the photographer. The stone columns and chains still exist today and surround areas of the car park in the Crosslink.*

21   *This view of the quadrangle shows the centre blocks of the side range between the two ward blocks A and B (previously E and F) that were much reduced in size from the original design. The water tower dominates the skyline and at the top of the quadrangle can be seen a patients' pavilion surrounded by hedging.*

10

22 *Features can be seen in this 1956 view that have long disappeared. Top right are the tennis courts and the patients' airing ground. In the centre are houses 11 and 12. In between can be seen the remnants of the lunatics' airing ground. Far right is the bomb-damaged area where the hospital museum once stood. Work is underway to remove the chimneys and replace the roof of B (previously F) Block. The double block structure with courtyards between is clearly visible.*

23 *An aerial view from the south shows the size and extent of the hospital and grounds. At the top is Brunel's gunboat yard (left) and HMS* Hornet *(right). In the foreground is the Psychiatric block known as G Block (left) and Canada Block (right).*

24 *A view of the staff tennis courts in 1976 that was soon to disappear with the building of the new galley and mess complex.*

26 *Much of the layout of the hospital has changed around the original building by 2003. On the left is the 1976 build with galley, messes and stores. In the centre is the Crosslink, completed in 1984. The number of parking spaces continues to increase.*

25 *E (previously C) Block and the original entrance to the Medical Officers Mess. The arched doorway and columns were retained when the block was refurbished in 1970. The Medical Officers Mess moved to a new building in 1899.*

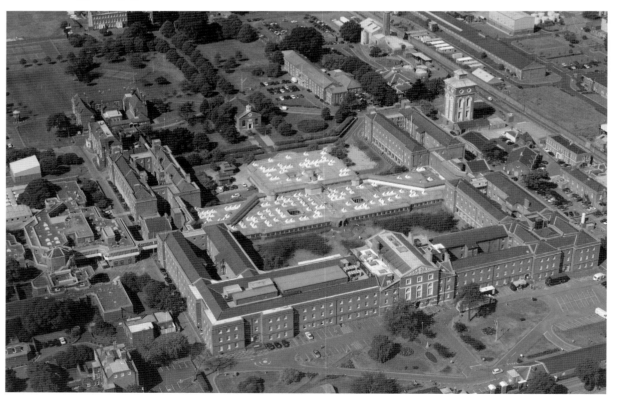

12

Hospital Interiors

When completed in 1762, Haslar had 114 wards, the majority having 19 or 20 beds, giving a capacity of a little over 2,000 beds. The maximum number a little later was probably nearer 2,500. Many of the original wards were in pairs, joined end on by a communicating door. Later these pairs were opened into single large wards, in use until the closure of the hospital.

In the early years the majority of patients were fever cases. The most contagious cases were, in 1787, confined to the upper wards and moved towards the ground floor for convalescence to give access to the open air. There were separate galleries for walking for patients recovering from measles, scabies, venereal disease and smallpox.

The arcade in the centre of the main façade was the entry point to the hospital with the receiving room and administrative offices opening onto the arcade.

In time, surgery became more common, initially performed amongst the other patients on the wards; the first operating theatres opened in 1897 above the arcade and overlooked the quadrangle. At this time, separation of the wards into Medical and Surgical became the norm.

The centre block over the arcade also contained the original X-ray department, opposite the theatres and, on the top floor, the first central galley.

27 *This is one of the earliest photographs of a ward in Haslar. Patients are in hospital gowns, some sitting by their beds, others huddled around the ward stove. The centre ward door is open and we can look through into the next ward. In this picture the beds have day covers. The floor is of teak and patients would heat a poker and touch the knots in the wooden floor to make them sing.*

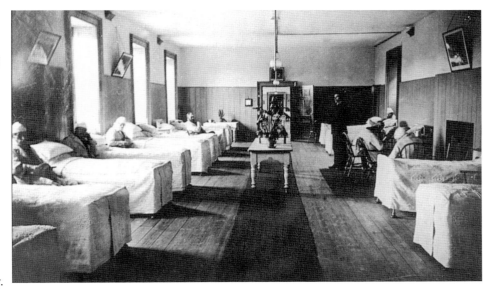

28 *Benbow Pensioners Ward with a Nursing Sister and Sick Berth Staff in a posed picture for the* Army and Navy Illustrated *of 1897. Naval Pensioners were admitted to Haslar to be cared for in the twilight of their days in special pensioner wards. Many passed the day waiting for a meal or, better still, their Grog ration, over which they relived their days at sea.*

29 *A ward stove, always glowing hot on winter days with patients huddled around them. It was the job of staff going on duty to carry scuttles of coal to the wards. This is a picture of the last remaining stove on A5 (until recently Day Surgery theatres) prior to its refurbishment in 1969.*

30 *On this ward the patients are of differing ages. Three Sick Berth Attendants stand to one side with another in the centre. The patients are in serge hospital uniform with hospital slippers and smocks. Some have head or arm injuries. Patients remained until completely recovered from their illness or injury and shorter hospital stays were uncommon before the 1970s.*

14

31 *With everything spick and span, this is a showpiece ward after 1905 and with electric light. The QARNNS Sister and Sick Berth Staff are wearing ward smocks and the patients wear hospital uniform and smocks. Two of the original wards have been joined, the connecting door replaced by an arch.*

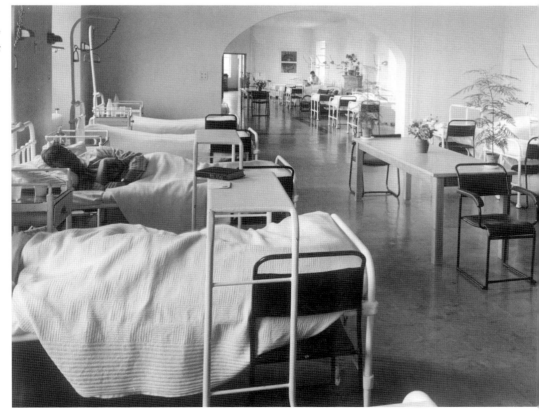

32 *A 1960s view of a ward with plants still permitted. In the distance a fireplace can be seen. The teak flooring is now covered with linoleum tiles which would be cleaned daily by the ward staff.*

33   *A 21st-century picture showing NHS staff on an orthopaedic ward.*

34   *NHS staff with a QARANC colleague on the Day Surgery Unit opened in 1998 on the first floor of D Block (previously A2 and 5).*

35   *RAMC and MOD civilian staff working together in the Clinical Measurements department.*

36   *A cheerful group of Royal Navy, QARANC and civilian staff on E5 (previously C5). This was the last ward to be modernised before closure in 2009.*

37   *Royal Navy, Royal Air Force and civilian Radiography staff pose in one of the X-Ray suites. The skeleton, rear centre, is understood not to be a member of staff.*

38   *The office of the Medical Officer in Charge in 1956, complete with name boards of previous Officers in Charge and the Queen Anne coat of arms that had been in the hospital since 1809. Through the window can be seen the quadrangle and ward Blocks E and F (previously C and D) in the distance.*

39   *In the cellars is the stout support for the hospital above. The bricks were hand-made from local clay.*

40 *The cellar under E (previously C) Block. This huge area below the original Medical Mess is thought to have been a storage space. The room in the distance through the doorway was used during the Second World War for underground operating theatres.*

41 *No Escape! The two Cellar corridors under C and D Blocks (previously B and A) run towards the Arcade underground and serve a series of vaulted rooms that were once used for anatomical dissection. The lower windows are barred to deter escape and can be bolted shut with original shutters. To the left and right are wooden piles in the brickwork. Many door lintels in the cellar are made from oak taken from hulks in the harbour.*

42　*In 1957 C (previously B) Block, where the hospital's second operating theatre complex was located, underwent a total refurbishment. Wooden stairs were replaced by a modern oval staircase with a ceiling light. This staircase has been admired by students of modern architecture but not by those who suffer from vertigo.*

43　*Haslar Museum was founded in 1827. It was situated in the block between E and F (previously C and D) Blocks. During the 19th century thousands of natural history specimens were sent back to Haslar by expeditions, including those of Sir John Richardson.*

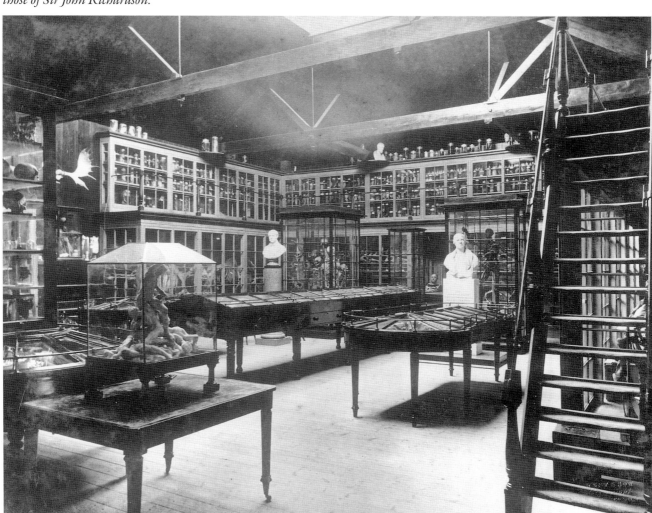

44 *The first curator of the museum was Charles Barron. Despite having only two fingers on one hand and none on the other he was skilled in the preparation of specimens. Sadly the museum was destroyed in 1941 in a bombing raid. Staff who emerged from the shelters the next morning reported seeing many specimens hanging from trees in the quadrangle. A museum curiosity, the four-footed duck, was never seen again.*

45 *The hospital laundry, 1897.*

46 *The hospital galley in the 19th century.*

47 *Containers stand ready to hold the next meal for delivery to the wards.*

20

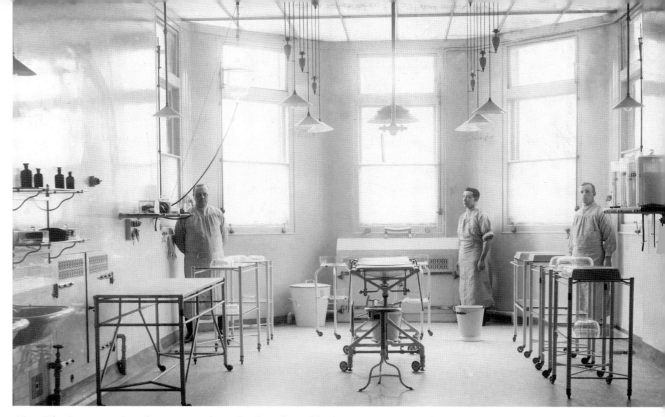

48 *The first operating theatre was above the Arcade and had a conservatory-style extension to admit more light. King George V visited the theatre in 1910. The brass stool, seen in the picture under the operating table, was still in use in the 1960s.*

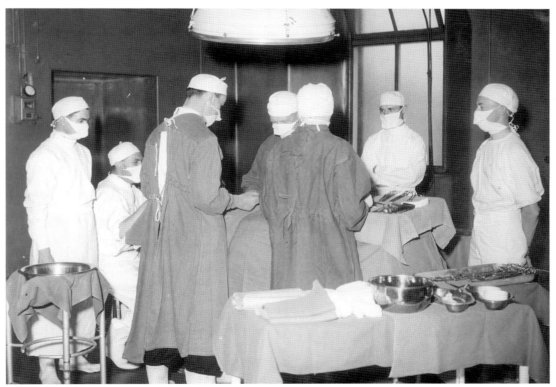

49 *The operating theatre in Sick Officers Block. This may be a recruiting picture. Surgeon Lieutenant Allan Tooley poses with SBAs Pat Smith, opposite (assisting), and left to right, George Hampton, Ron Brown, at the head of the table, and Arthur Fox, looking on with other unnamed colleagues.*

50 *The Pathology Department, 1897.*

51 *The Pharmacy, situated in the same building as the Pathology Department.*

52 *Surgeon Commander Edward Atkinson DSO, AM, Polar Medal RN 1882-1928. He joined the Royal Navy in 1908 and was appointed to Haslar as the Vaccinator in the Pathology Department. In 1910 he joined the* Terra Nova *for Captain Scott's ill-fated Antarctic expedition. Left in charge of the base camp, it was Atkinson who organised the search party that found the body of Scott. Atkinson served at Gallipoli and was awarded the DSO for conspicuous bravery at the Battle of the Somme and the Albert Medal for saving lives on board HMS* Glatton *after she caught fire in 1918.*

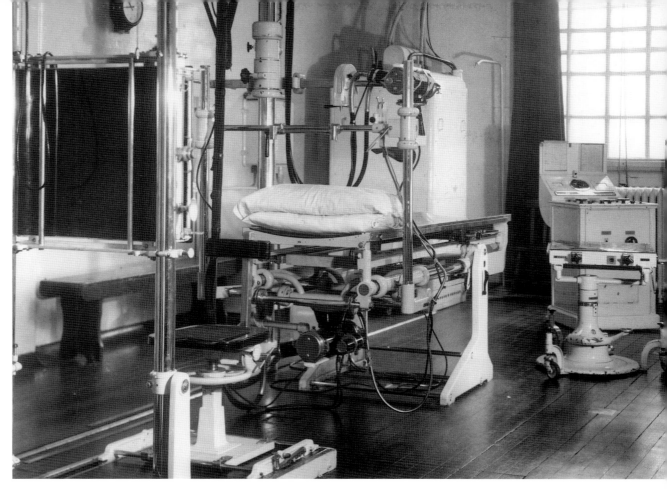

53   *The X-Ray Department in the centre block over the Arcade. This was later occupied by Nuclear Medicine following the transfer of X-Ray to the Crosslink in 1984.*

54   *The Gymnasium on the ground floor of B (previously F) Block in the 1950s.*

55   *The Physiotherapy Department. A posed picture taken for the first prospectus of the Royal Navy Physiotherapy School. The picture shows patients, one in battle dress, undergoing treatment. Physiotherapists, a QARNNS Nursing Sister and a Naval Nurse are in attendance.*

56   *Occupational Therapy workshop on the ground floor of E (previously C) Block. Patients stayed in hospital for many months and occupational therapy included activities such as carpentry, weaving and basket making.*

57 *A staircase in D (previously A) Block in the 1960s. This was one of the last original staircases in the block and was unpainted. After demolition during the re-build in 1969, part of the balustrade was made into the altar rail of St Luke's Church.*

58 *The last remaining original staircases are in F (previously D) Block. Their survival is because this part of the hospital was used for many years as nurses quarters. James Lind in conversation with John Howard, the prison and hospital reformer, stated in 1780, 'That in the summer he would have the windows on the stairs of the hospital nailed open for the want of fresh air'.*

59 *The supporting structure of the galley complex on the top floor above the Arcade. This area was later occupied by Sterile Services. Oak timbers taken from hulks were used alongside new wood.*

60   *The Attics were used for staff and patient accommodation. Windows opened into the inner courtyard.*

61   *In the centre block, over the main Arcade, the shaft from the ground floor to the roof was designed to admit light and fresh air.*

St Luke's and St Mary's

St Luke's was completed in 1756 and, had the fourth side of the quadrangle been completed, would have been at its centre.

Through the main doors the visitor passes under the gallery, which was reduced from its original size when the church was totally rebuilt internally in 1963-4 following infestation by death watch beetle. Much of the original undressed stonework from the floor of the church was reused in the refurbishment, which was carried out under the supervision of Mr Ken Makins, the Diocesan Surveyor. The church was rededicated on 18 October 1964 by the Right Reverend J.H.L. Phillips, Bishop of Portsmouth, and Raymond Richardson, Chaplain of the Fleet.

The area between E and D (previously C and F) Blocks originally held the Hospital Museum but this was destroyed by bombing in 1941. Later, St Mary's Roman Catholic Church was here, remaining until the construction of the Crosslink. The church was succeeded by St Mary's Chapel in C (previously B) Block, which continued to function until the closure of the hospital.

62 St Luke's in the 1880s. Note the rendered brickwork. The iron railings enabled patients to be confined in the quadrangle. A gate permitted access to St Luke's and the railings survived until around 1905.

63 *An Edwardian view of St Luke's. The rendering has been removed. Ivy covers the brickwork.*

64 *A view of both St Luke's and Admiral's Walk. In the foreground can be seen the main sewer grating set into the pathway. The sewers were utilised by patients for escape and by nursing staff to smuggle liquor into the hospital.*

65 The inside of St Luke's prior to refurbishment. The balcony reaches further into the body of the church and is approached by dual staircases. Those attending church in the 18th and 19th centuries knew their place. Physicians and their patients sat to one side of the aisle, whilst the surgeons and their patients sat on the other side. Labourers sat in the balcony.

66 A pre-1963 view of the aisle and altar. Note the choir stalls and the Haywood Hardy painting in situ behind the altar.

67 A mid-refurbishment view. About a third of the original brickwork was replaced.

68 A mid-refurbishment view looking towards the altar end. The stained glass windows have been removed.

29

69 *View of the altar from the aisle prior to refurbishment. The baldacchino over the altar was erected in 1920 as a First World War Memorial, having been designed by the architect Sir Charles Nicholson. It has octagonal Corinthian columns.*

70 *The stained glass windows on either side of the canopy depict the four evangelists and were dedicated by the Chaplain of the Fleet on 10 April 1910 to the memory of Medical Officers who had died on active service.*

71 *'The Healing of Blind Bartimaeus' was painted by Heywood Hardy RA (1842-1933) and is considered by Osbert Sitwell as one of his finest works. The painting was removed from behind the altar and placed into the side chapel under the balcony. Wrought ironwork by Mr Ken Ball, Hospital Blacksmith, can be seen to the left.*

72 *St Luke's in winter sunshine, with Sick Officers Block in the background. The ship's bell, captured at the Second Battle of Copenhagen in 1807 from the 80-gun Danish ship* King Christian VII, *stands in the foreground. The ship became a hospital hulk in the River Medway and when she was broken up in 1837 the bell was moved to Haslar. The bell has recently been returned to the Danish Navy.*

73 *The assembled clergy at the final service held on 30 March 2007. The Reverend John Hill, the last Chaplain, is third from the left.*

74 *Surgeon Captain James Campbell, Commanding Officer Royal Hospital Haslar and Fort Blockhouse, watches as the Reverend Monsignor Paul Donovan, Principal Roman Catholic Chaplain to the Navy, turns the key in the main door to mark the closure of St Luke's.*

75 *The late Commander Ian Coulton receives the key to St Luke's from Surgeon Captain Campbell.*

76 *The interior of St Mary's Roman Catholic Church.*

77 *The entrance to St Mary's Church was close to the entrance to the Nurses Quarters, with a notice on the wall that stated 'Out of Bounds to Male Personnel except on duty'. The open area in the foreground was the site of the museum and undeveloped for forty years.*

78 *St Mary's Chapel on the first floor of C (previously B) Block in the hospital replaced St Mary's Church.*

RESIDENCES

During the early years of the hospital all staff, including families and servants, were accommodated within the main range of the hospital. In March 1756 construction began on four residences, two at either end of the main façade of the hospital.

These residences face each other. For those looking at the front of the hospital, the residences to the left were later known as Houses 11 and 12 and those to the right as Houses 13 and 14.

Following a board of enquiry in 1794, the management of the hospital was, for a period of 75 years, removed from medical officers in favour of executive command by serving Naval Captains. As a result, Earl Spencer, accompanied by other Lords of the Admiralty, marked out the ground for erecting the houses for the Governor, Lieutenants and other officers on 1 October 1795.

The Terrace was built from 1796 to 1798, occupying an area to the south-west of the hospital previously used as a burial ground.

79 *James Lind (1716-94) became known as the Father of Nautical Medicine. He was the second Physician in Charge of Haslar from June 1758 to June 1783 when his son John succeeded him. James Lind's paper on Scurvy, resulting from work undertaken on board HMS* Salisbury, *preceded his time at Haslar although many of the patients he treated were suffering from scurvy. Whilst at Haslar he ensured that the fleet blockading Brest was supplied with fresh fruit and vegetables.*

80   *Houses 13 and 14 at the north-west end of the main façade of the hospital. James Lind is believed to have occupied one of these houses. Later, house 14 was the official residence of the Medical Officer in Charge of the Hospital.*

81   *Houses 11 and 12. A photograph taken in 1880. On the right-hand side can be seen the extension built by Sir John Richardson to accommodate his large family.*

82   *The south-west side of Sir John Richardson's extension overlooked the lunatics' airing ground. His son, also John, recalled his childhood much later in 1916:*

> *On the side of our garden lay the grounds of the lunatic asylum. These and their inmates had a strange fascination for me. When my father first went to Haslar, the asylum was under the charge of a medical officer who apparently held the view that lunacy could be cured or controlled only by the administration of severe disciplinary measures, and the unfortunate men were sadly knocked about by the attendants. My father's righteous soul was vexed with what he saw, for much was viewed from the verandah of our house, though hardly as much as what I could see from a perch on a ladder against the garden wall.*
>
> *As soon as the lunatics were let out of the wards in the morning, some of them took up set places in the grounds. One poor fellow for years occupied a corner under our garden wall, where he swayed incessantly from one leg to the other. The men never seemed to quarrel or interfere with each other's pitches, but they occasionally knocked down an attendant who was cruel to them, when they were, in the early days, punished with blows, solitary confinement and strait-waistcoats.*

83   *Sir John Richardson (1787-1865) entered the Royal Navy in 1807, as a surgeon's mate, becoming a full surgeon the following year. After 1815, he was on half pay in Scotland, returning to the Navy as Surgeon-Naturalist for Sir John Franklin's first and second Arctic expeditions. He was later to participate, at the age of 61, in one of the unsuccessful attempts to find the ill-fated Franklin expedition. His travels enabled him to bring many specimens to the museum in Haslar. Before Haslar, he had administered the Melville Hospital (later RNH) in Chatham. At Haslar his duties were as Physician but the arrival of another Arctic explorer, Sir William Edward Parry, as Superintendent at the hospital allowed the relationship between clinical and administrative staff to improve.*

84   *The covered balcony to the rear of Richardson's residence:*

> *The walled garden of our house was marvellous in the fruit line. I have never seen its like since. Grapes grew and generally ripened on the south wall; plums, peaches, apples, pear, and figs were produced in any quantity and of splendid quality. In those days Officers held their appointments practically for life, and consequently took much pains with their official properties. I may mention that the excellent productive qualities of our garden were deemed due to the liberal quantity of cow manure and seaweed available; the latter came in cartloads from Haslar beach.*

85   *The stable block to the rear of Richardson's residence.*

86 The Terrace. The main residence in the centre of the Terrace was occupied initially by Governors but later by Superintendents, Inspectors General of Hospitals and Fleets, Surgeons-General, Surgeon Rear Admirals in Charge and Medical Directors General, Royal Navy.

SURGEON REAR ADMIRAL'S RESIDENCE

87 Surgeon Rear Admiral's plaque above the door to the residence.

88 The Terrace in 1976.

89 A Victorian view of the Terrace showing the white railings at the front, later removed for wartime recycling. Officers Terraces similar to this one are also found in the dockyards at Portsmouth and Chatham.

90 *A modern view of the houses that make up the Terrace. The pebble dash is one attempt at making the house waterproof, a problem since construction.*

CAPTAIN PARRY.

Published November 7, 1823 by G. Smeeton, Arcade, Pall Mall.

91 *An 1823 engraving of Captain William Edward Parry, Naval Hydrographer and famous Arctic explorer, who came to Haslar in 1846 as Captain Superintendent. Parry was, perhaps, the most distinguished resident of the Terrace, although his introduction of compulsory sea-bathing for patients and staff may have received a mixed reaction. Sir John Richardson's son describes the effect that Parry had on the hospital:*

> *There was fairly constant friction between the fighting and healing forces – chiefly, I think, because the Captains and Lieutenants made sorties into the wards and domains of the medical staffs, sorties which were not always beneficial to the patients; or because the Captain would send for the Medical Officers in a body to his office to hear his wisdom when they were busy with visits, operations, post mortems, or instruction. But, though the governing system remained the same, all friction disappeared when Sir Edward Parry, the great Arctic explorer, became Captain Superintendent.*
>
> *He was a most genial man, and tactful, so that very soon the most excellent relations existed between him and officers of the medical staff. He affected considerable reforms in consultation with the staff – indeed, one and all in Haslar loved him and his family. Haslar became a different place officially and socially.*

92 *The rear of the Surgeon Rear Admiral's residence in summer.*

93 *The Surgeon Rear Admiral's garden looking into the walled garden and to the hospital paddock beyond.*

38

Victorian and Edwardian Expansion

The Georgian hospital, including the Terrace, had been constructed over a period of fifty years and was completed by the end of the 18th century. It served well the needs of the patients during the Napoleonic Wars, after which there was a period of relative calm.

The Crimean War and other later 19th-century conflicts provided the impetus for a second period of building.

94   *The Laundry was built in 1854 to replace the hospital wash house of 1756, now known as Haslar Cottages. At the top right in the roof can be seen the water tank fed from a well just inside the Gunboat Yard across Haslar Road. The tall chimney belongs to Isambard Kingdom Brunel's engine house that powered a travelator to move Gun Boats. Some washer staff caught typhus from used hospital sheets and clothing, a number dying and being buried in the hospital grounds.*

95   *A view of the Laundry from Haslar Road showing the water tank in the roof and bricked up windows and what was an original entrance through the hospital wall. The wall has in the past been scaled by escaping patients. The Guard and Police patrolled the wall and on occasion cut down the escape ropes. Sometimes up to fifty men went over the wall, returning later somewhat the worse for drink!*

96 *The Hospital Chapel of Rest (1868) with the Post Mortem Room behind and the Water Tower in the distance.*

97 *Hospitals use a lot of water. In the early 1900s the daily consumption of water in Haslar was estimated at 51 gallons per head. Early shallow wells were less than satisfactory both in volume and quality of water. A new well was sunk in 1859 to a depth of 340 feet with a spring being found at 212 feet.*

The water tower was completed in 1885 and is 120 feet high, with two 125-ton water tanks each holding 50,000 gallons.

The tower is a well-known landmark and was used in the Second World War by the Luftwaffe on bombing runs heading for Portsmouth Dockyard. A former German bomber pilot visited the hospital in the 1980s and asked to see the water tower.

98 *The Sisters' Mess was built in 1899. A rose garden is in the foreground. The mess was later named after Mrs Eliza Mackenzie who, along with her clergyman husband and six trained nurses, had been sent by the Admiralty to set up a Naval Hospital at Therapia during the Crimean War.*

99 *Entrance to the Edwardian covered way that leads to the Medical and Sisters' Mess from the colonnaded area under F (previously D) Block.*

100 *The covered way looking forwards to the Medical Mess. The Sisters' Mess is to the left.*

101 *The Medical Mess was completed in 1902. The Sisters' Mess can be seen on the right. In this picture there are four grass tennis courts. There was also a croquet lawn. Two Medical Officers sit under a small tent in uniform, one reading a paper, the other dozing in the sun.*

102 *The Medical Mess with G Block (Psychiatric) and the Sentry Post in the background. Gone are the grass tennis courts and ivy-strewn walls.*

103 *The stores at the front of the hospital date from 1853. From these stores all items required to support the hospital were issued. A similar adjacent store area was used to house patients' baggage. In the 20th century the stores held medical supplies that were distributed to ships and naval units worldwide.*

104 *Building 40, as it came to be known, was built in1899 as the administrative block of the Zymotic (or Infectious) Diseases Hospital. After the closure of the Zymotics, this building supported the offices of the Surgeon Rear Admiral Medical Services and in later years became the Estate Management offices. Gone are the rail tracks that were either side of the rose beds.*

105 *The Haslar foreshore with the Zymotic Hospital and Old Portsmouth beyond. To the left, in the foreground, can be seen part of Haslar Barracks, once an Army Hospital and later Haslar Prison.*

106 *A rear view of the Zymotic Hospital with building 40 in the background. On the left is the surrounding wall that separated the Zymotics from the main hospital. To the right of the wall can be seen one of the support buildings containing the galley and stores.*

107 *Front view of the Zymotic Blocks with upper-floor verandahs where patients would sit in all weathers taking the sea air while looking out over the Solent to Spithead.*

Prior to the construction of the Zymotic Hospital, it was necessary to exhume 26 Turkish sailors who had been buried here in 1850 (including the Captain of one ship) after being admitted to Haslar with typhus. The two Turkish ships were in Portsmouth to train with the Royal Navy. After exhumation in 1899, the Turks were reburied at Clayhall in a separate Turkish Plot.

During and after the Second World War the Zymotic hospital was known as 'M' Block and became a Night Duty staff block using some ward areas for accommodation.

108 *All goods could be passed to the Zymotic Hospital through a purpose-built hole in the boundary wall in order to prevent cross-infection. Patients admitted to Zymotics were bathed on arrival and their clothes washed in Lysol.*

109 *The newly built Pathology Block, 1899. The alignment of this building is different from all others in that it faces due south to provide the best light for microscopy. In the foreground is a small fir tree, since grown in stature and now towering above the surrounding buildings.*

110 *Main Pathology Block. Built in the mid-19th century, this building served both as a laboratory and pharmacy during the Victorian era. It reverted to a pharmacy in the mid-20th century and more recently has been a Pathology administration support block.*

111 *Sick Officers Block of 1904. This view was taken in 1976 when the block was being used as Nurses Quarters.*

112 *The newly opened Sick Officers Block stands ready to receive patients. The building housed a series of four-, two- and single-bedded cabins with senior officers accommodated in the front and junior officers at the rear. The building had an operating theatre and a galley with stewards and staff to wait on the patients. The upper floor was served by a rickety iron-gated lift. Later, a series of TB cabins stood in the grounds behind the main building.*

113 *A posed photograph shows a Sub Lieutenant in a bath chair with visitors. Sick Berth Staff and nurses look on from the balcony. Most of the hospital blocks were given alphabetical identifiers and the Sick Officers Block was known as Q Block.*

114 *G Psychiatric Block opened in 1910 complete with padded cell. This is the successor to the Asylum that had been on the ground floor of E (previously C) Block in the main hospital. Like many external blocks it also accommodated night duty staff. It has also been used as nurses accommodation.*

115   *G Block from the seaward side, with Eliza Mackenzie House in the background on the right. The open grounds give splendid views of Spithead.*

116   *Erroll Hall was opened in 1913 following a bequest from the widow of Commander George Erroll RN, who had died in service. It was used as a library, for snooker and billiards and as a rest centre for patients. The main hall had a stage and changing rooms and up until the 1950s was regularly used for the entertainment of both patients and staff. BBC broadcasts from the Hall featured well known acts such as Flanagan and Allen, Cyril Fletcher, Arthur Askey and the Memphis Boys. At Christmas pantomimes were staged. In recent years the Hall became a staff gymnasium.*

Canada Block

When Haslar opened staff were housed within the main building. By the start of the 20th century new messes had been built for Medical Officers and Nursing Sisters. The remaining nurses eventually moved into F (previously D) Block, but it was not until 1917 that Sick Berth Staff had their own quarters.

In Canada, during the First World War, the Imperial Order of the Daughters of the Empire was keen to contribute to the war effort. The Order raised significant sums and £50,000 of this was earmarked to allow the number of beds at Haslar to be increased by 250. After consideration, it was realised that the best way to increase the number was to build staff accommodation and thus free space within the main building.

The new building was named Women of Canada Block though this was abbreviated to 'Canada Block'. The eventual cost was £38,000, the sum approved to build the original hospital in the 18th century. The remaining money was used to open two new wards at the Royal Naval Hospital, Chatham.

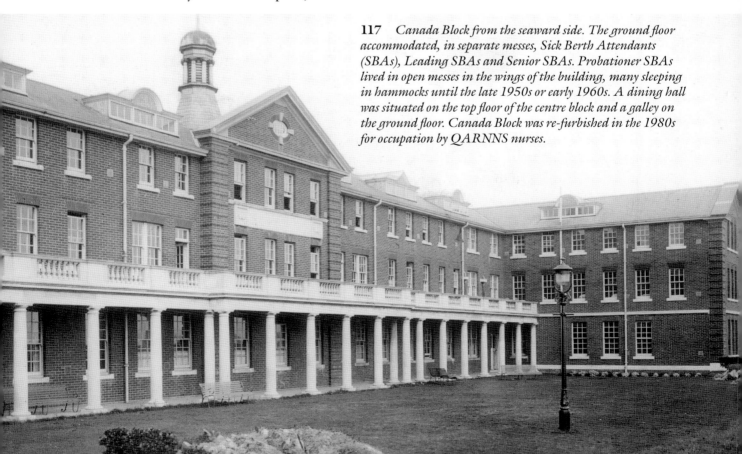

117 *Canada Block from the seaward side. The ground floor accommodated, in separate messes, Sick Berth Attendants (SBAs), Leading SBAs and Senior SBAs. Probationer SBAs lived in open messes in the wings of the building, many sleeping in hammocks until the late 1950s or early 1960s. A dining hall was situated on the top floor of the centre block and a galley on the ground floor. Canada Block was re-furbished in the 1980s for occupation by QARNNS nurses.*

118 *'From the Women of Canada', an Expression of Love and Loyalty for King and Empire. Complete with maple leaves, this panel is situated over the first floor of the building facing out to sea and extolling undying gratitude for the brave. The Imperial Order of the Daughters of the Empire still send Christmas vouchers to all Canadian Veterans living overseas in gratitude for the service given and to show they are not forgotten. A maple tree was planted in the grounds in recent years by the Canadian Ambassador.*

119 *This is believed to be a celebration tea after the unveiling of the new Shelter presented by the Ladies Needlework Guild seen in the top right corner of the picture.*

120 *The plaque inside the Shelter, which is still in use today. Lady Colville was the wife of the Commander in Chief Portsmouth, who was to become ADC to King George V.*

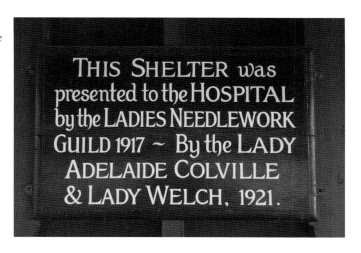

THIS SHELTER was
presented to the HOSPITAL
by the LADIES NEEDLEWORK
GUILD 1917 ~ By the LADY
ADELAIDE COLVILLE
& LADY WELCH, 1921.

121 *The Shelter today with the plaque visible though the window. In the distance stands another shelter or pavilion facing towards the Solent and used on occasions by staff, patients and families.*

122   *The Junior Sick Berth Staff bar in the early 1960s, the scene of many a good evening, especially in 'blank week' (staff were paid fortnightly and the week before payday was known as 'blank week'). On pay day and the weekend that ensued, Gosport and Portsmouth were lively. The following week the bar was the place for a cheap beer and entertainment.*

123   *Upper Mess of Canada Block in the late 1960s. Large wardrobes were the order of the day, a change from the tin lockers previously in use. The wardrobes could be placed to give some privacy. The metal bars once supported hammocks but they became an assault course when many young SBAs challenged each other to a 'Tarzan swing' from one end of the mess to the other. Some made it, others did not!*

No pin-ups here, just a Navy News *calendar and, further over, a collection of 'Easy Rider' posters.*

124   *The top floor Junior SBA and Probationers dining room. In the 1960s a dining room assistant known as 'One Eyed Fred' worked here. At meal times he would shout, 'You lucky people' as he served out the meals. Fred had a glass eye which frequently found its way onto new joiners' plates.*

CROSSLINK

The advent of the National Health Service in 1948 allowed military patients to be admitted to civilian hospitals and civilian patients to be admitted to service hospitals. This arrangement was not formalised until 1967 when approval for Haslar to provide beds for between 85 and 105 civilian patients was given.

The change from a purely Royal Naval Hospital to a district general hospital, now catering for women and children, and the need for better X-ray, accident and emergency and operating theatre facilities, drove the need for expansion. After a feasibility study, the decision was taken to join the two side ranges of the original hospital at their mid-points. This improved movement within the hospital by providing an efficient functional nucleus. At the same time, replacement of the galley, stores and some staff accommodation in the older parts of the hospital could be undertaken on the former airing grounds to the south-east of the hospital towards the seawall. The main entrance to the hospital was moved to Haslar Road, with the original gates being retained for ceremonial purposes.

The foundation of the Crosslink was laid in June 1980 and the new building was opened by Admiral Sir John Fieldhouse in April 1984.

125 *A general view of the hospital quadrangle in 1979 before the bulldozers moved in to begin building the Crosslink. The photograph was taken from the top of the centre block over the Arcade. On the right are red milk crates stacked against the wall of the victualling office and next door, with the green shrubbery, is the Matrons House, all of which was to disappear with the new build. In the top section of lawn is the shrub border that once surrounded a patients' pavilion. The trees of Admiral's Walk are no longer pruned.*

126 *A JCB starts to break down the central area between E and F (previously C and D) Blocks and soon St Mary's Church would be no more. The construction of the cellars of the Crosslink is in progress and many bones are said to have been found during excavation.*

127 *The completed Crosslink prior to opening in April 1984.*

128 *A view of the Crosslink from St Luke's Church, with the five new main operating theatres on the first floor. Below are the services for the whole building. The pathway leads from the church and the design of the building was such that you could walk the route of the old Admiral's Walk towards the original (ceremonial) gates. It was intended that the Church should be visible from the gates, but in practice this was only possible if all the doors were open at the same time.*

AIRING THE PATIENTS

Throughout the history of the hospital there has been an emphasis on allowing patients access to the grounds for recreation. From Victorian times ample fresh air was considered beneficial to the treatment of tuberculosis in particular. At times, sea-bathing was also encouraged. The Zymotic Hospital on the sea-wall had balconies to encourage patients to take the sea air.

129 *An Edwardian picture of patients strolling in the hospital grounds in front of the Terrace. The newly opened Sick Officers Block (1904) can be seen through the trees. The patients are dressed in Hospital Uniform, a blue shirt and blue serge jacket and trousers. This area had a patients' pathway, seen here just beyond the fence, forming a circuit around this part of the grounds. Old plans of this area show a water trough for cattle. Excavation of the area in recent years exposed the pathway and artefacts such as brass buttons from hospital uniforms and a pipe cleaning knife.*

130 *Patients and Staff, Open Air Ward. This area is in front of the old D Block, now F Block, and the remains of the open ward can still be seen. Patients suffering from tuberculosis were believed to benefit from being nursed in the open air and this area had a shelter with a screen that dropped down in inclement weather. The Wellcome Museum holds paintings of Haslar by a First World War artist. One painting is of this open air ward.*

131 *A pre-First World War postcard showing the open air ward with patients and Sick Berth Staff. One bed patient has been pushed over to join the group. The screens can be seen rolled up and tied and the patients' beds all made under the sloping roof of the ward. One wonders if the patients managed to eat their meals in the warm somewhere.*

132 *This photograph with Canada Block in the background was taken in 1976. It shows the area of the open air ward seen in the previous two pictures. The tree in the centre which was just a small tree in the postcard has grown somewhat over fifty years. It is now found next to the former Medical Mess annexe, which was connected to the new galley complex.*

133 *A patients' pavilion in the area near Canada Block. Two such pavilions were built in the mid-19th century for the use of patients. This one is in the area that was near the Lunatics Airing Ground. The pavilions were raised on earth mounds and gave views over the boundary wall to Spithead. In later years the pavilion was also a popular place in the evening for courting staff, as were the airing grounds in general.*

134 *The second pavilion was built further along the sea-wall area in the open grounds opposite the sentry post. This picture, taken in the late 19th century, shows not only a huge mound of cut grass but a group of patients in hospital clothing posing for the camera. It gives a feel of a well kept country estate. By 1910 G Block was built a few yards to the left of this pavilion.*

135 *The same pavilion as in the previous photograph in a picture taken specifically for the* Navy and Army Illustrated *of 1897. Once again, patients pose and take their ease mostly in hospital uniform, but some are in naval rig and a Marine stands in the background by the pavilion.*

136 Each block in the main body of the hospital had an open area on the ground floor facing the quadrangle. In this area patients could sit, especially in inclement weather, and chat and swap tales whilst puffing a pipe and perhaps downing a tot or two from their daily ration of rum. Most of these areas were enclosed as the demand for office and departmental space increased in the 1950s.

137 In the 1920s a new pavilion was built on the sea-wall in the area opposite the entrance to *HMS* Dolphin.

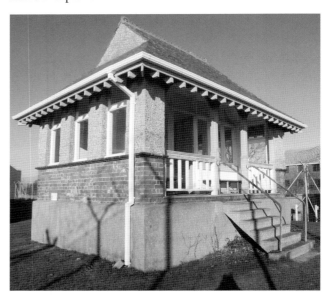

138 A patient in a wheel chair and a nursing attendant pose for a photograph on Admiral's Walk. With pollarded trees and neat and tidy grounds the quadrangle was the perfect place for patients and staff to stroll. St Luke's in the background is part-covered with ivy.

139 An Edwardian view of the quadrangle from the top of the main Arcade, or centre block, as it was also known. Either side of Admiral's Walk can be seen two patients' pavilions surrounded by hedging. Benches and seats are arranged around the outside of the pavilions.

AROUND THE GROUNDS

Ihere is probably no other hospital in the United Kingdom as well provided with exercising grounds for the patients as Haslar, a circumstance which does great credit to the wisdom of its founders. The 'Airing ground', as it is called in old documents, is nearly a mile in circumference. The portion between the south wing and the sea is provided with two mounds, with summer houses or smoking pavilions on top, from whence delightful views are obtained of Spithead, the Isle of Wight and Southsea beach. These are popular lounges, and during smoking hours the greater part of the convalescents congregate here. A portion of the enclosure is reserved for officers, who can enjoy a stroll and a smoke under pleasanter conditions than are often vouchsafed to them afloat. The trees afford abundance of shade, or shelter from the winds, and were it not for the inevitable monotony of existence under conditions inseparable from a state of disablement, the lot of the patient at Haslar might almost seem an enviable one.

Navy and Army Illustrated Friday 19 February 1897.

140   *The Sentry Post or Gazebo in the late 1880s. It stands inside a fenced area of the grounds with entry gained through a rotating stile. St Luke's Church can be seen on the left with the newly built water tower (1885) in the distance. The Gazebo dates from the late 18th century and may have been used to provide a watch over patients. At times it was also used as a bandstand for entertainment in the First World War. Patients were able to look out over Spithead and the Solent from this vantage point.*

*   The Medical and Sisters' Mess had been built by 1899 and this view changed. Note the metal fence on the right that stretched across the top of the hospital quadrangle and in front of St Luke's. This design of metal bench seat can still be seen around the hospital grounds.*

142 *A view from the Gazebo towards the Terrace with grass tennis courts in the foreground, 1976. These were later replaced by hard courts. Many of the large trees fell in the storm of October 1987.*

142 *A late Victorian picture of the road to the Terrace taken from the rear of St Luke's Church. A man in a bowler hat takes his ease by leaning on the fence for the photographer. A group of children are playing in the road close to the Terrace, and on either side of the picture in the distance can be seen high brick walls around the Paddock.*

143 *Taken before 1885 as the water tower is not present, this is one of the earliest photographs of St Luke's Church. A group of patients and perhaps staff pose along the iron fence over which can be seen the main hospital and the open space of the quadrangle. On the right-hand side of the quadrangle is the top of one of two patients' pavilions. In the centre is a tall post on top of which is a covered bell.*

144 *The meteorological station was situated where messes were built in 1899.*

145 *An Edwardian photograph of the ground staff tending the flower beds of the quadrangle. Haslar had a large civilian workforce who cared for the grounds, buildings and services required for the hospital. A horticultural centre was based in the present Memorial Garden with greenhouses and cold frames to produce both vegetables and flowers.*

146 *An Edwardian picture of the Medical Mess grass tennis courts. It is not easy to determine the difference between ground staff and officers.*

147 *This wonderful posed picture (c.1880) has been taken from the area of St Luke's Church looking towards the Sentry Post or Gazebo and the sea-wall. An elderly gentleman pensioner sits leaning on a cane and wearing a top hat, whilst other patients or pensioners sit in the long grass or look down from the post. In the distance is a large brick wall stretching along the sea-wall area. By 1899 this view had been changed with the building of the Zymotic (Infectious Diseases) Hospital.*

'Doc'

The establishment of a trained Sick Berth Staff for work in Naval Hospitals was authorised in 1884. In 1891 Sick Berth personnel were given new style uniforms, double-breasted jackets as worn by Chief Petty Officers, and were given the name of 'Sick Bay Tiffy'. Staff were also addressed as 'Sick Bay Stewards', especially by Officers.

The name 'Doc' has been used for all who perform medical duties in the Royal Navy. This chapter contains photographs of Medical Officers and those known as 'Doc'.

148 *Haslar, 1897. Admiral Duncan Hilston poses with his Medical Officers at the front of the Hospital. In the background can be seen the sheds of the Gunboat yard. Far left middle row sits Commander Gimlette who was to become Inspector of Fleets and Hospitals based at Haslar. The vicar sitting upright in a mortar board and collar is the Reverend Octavius Rutherford Foster Hughes BA, vicar of St Luke's.*

149 *Medical Officers in the late 19th century. Note the variety of caps, collars and facial hair.*

150 *This picture is believed to be the earliest showing Sick Berth Staff at Haslar. They pose in fine fashion with their instructors in front of the main façade of the hospital. One of the senior rates has a chest full of medal ribbons and nearly all sport a watch chain on their waistcoats. This picture was taken when the staff lived in the upper floors of the main building of the hospital. It was acquired when a person arrived at the main gate of the hospital one day with an envelope of photos and said, 'Have these, one has my Great Grandfather on, he worked at Haslar', and then left.*

151 *An interesting photograph of a member of the Sick Berth Reserve who has First World War chevrons on his right sleeve.*

152 *Night duty staff, Christmas 1928. They are not in summer rig but in white trousers over which they would have worn ward gowns. All Sick Berth Staff wore 'Tiffs' rig as worn by Naval Artificers.*

153 *Young fresh-faced Sick Berth Probationers pose with Surgeon Rear Admiral Buckeridge, Medical Officer in Charge of Haslar, and instructors, in front of Canada Block in 1937.*

154 *The first class to accept civilians into the Royal Naval Physiotherapy School at Haslar, 1960s.*

155   *Wardmaster Officers were commissioned Sick Berth Staff. This photograph was probably taken in the early 1960s at the front of the hospital. Left to right, back: E. Bishop, J. Duncan, O. Saunders, S. Saunders; E. Fay. Front: J. Lihou, A. Masters, W. Ford, J. Stockton.*

156   *Over the years many photographs were taken in front of Canada Block. Training of Sick Berth Staff took place in what was known as* Dolphin II, *now occupied by the Royal Navy Submarine Museum, and classes would march from Haslar, cross the road for instruction, and return to Canada Block for meals and to sleep.*

QARNNS AND VADS

QARNNS (by Captain Julia Massey RRC)

The 18th- and early 19th-century nurses working in Haslar were mainly widows of sailors and marines or wives of serving sailors. Instructions given by the Commissioners stated that 'there shall be one nurse to attend fourteen patients and these nurses shall be the most sober careful and diligent that can be had'. In reality the nurses were not averse to stealing patients' property and forging their wills. Living locally they imported large quantities of gin, usually 'tied around their waist and under their stays in bladders'. In some months as much as six gallons was being seized by the hospital authorities. They were also open to bribery to help patients escape, and stole hospital food and items such as bedclothes and soap. One nurse was dismissed 'for going to bed with four or five patients and infecting one of them with the foul

157 *QARNNS 1887.*

'Miss Louisa Hogg (centre), Head Sister, Royal Hospital Haslar, with Nursing Sisters. Sisters were introduced into Naval Hospitals in 1885. Miss Hogg occupied this important position for a number of years. The presence of Sisters in the wards has a restraining influence on Jack's proverbial command of words; his expressions, when in familiar converse with his chums, being marked by aptness rather than elegance, while his "terms of endearment" would grate harshly on the refined ear.'

The Navy and Army Illustrated, *1897*

disease'. The conditions of service for these women were appalling and they were liable to be dismissed at will 'upon a decrease of patients'. When the Commissioners were prompted to ask in 1755 why so many nurses quit, the response was 'being confined and imprisoned and that they never eat a hot meal, and are served with scraps left by the seamen and are badly paid having but a trifle of wages when perhaps there is four of five months due'. In 1854 the female nurses were replaced by pensioners under the direction of a female matron.

Despite the success of Mrs Eliza Mackenzie and her nurses at the Naval Hospital at Therapia during the Crimean War it was to be thirty years before female nurses returned to Haslar, by which time nurses were being trained in civilian hospitals. A number of 'experienced Naval Medical Officers' were against the introduction of female nurses. In 1884 Miss Henrietta Stewart was appointed Head Sister at Haslar together with six Sisters. Miss Stewart was found to be unsuitable and dismissed and replaced in 1885 by Miss Belle Storey. In the wards the Sisters were addressed as Madam by both staff and patients and precautions were taken to protect them from viewing the middle third of a patient's body.

An important part of the Sisters' responsibility was the practical tuition of the Sick Berth Attendants. A report from Haslar about the Sisters referred to 'their professional knowledge and skill' as being of 'incalculable benefit' and that 'the mere presence of these ladies exercises a restraining and humanizing influence over the patients and this tends directly to the preservation of order and decency on the wards'.

In 1902, HM Queen Alexandra became President of the Naval Nursing Service and it became Queen Alexandra's Royal Naval Nursing Service (QARNNS). During the First World War Sisters continued to serve in Haslar and also abroad in hospital ships and RN establishments, augmented by reserve Sisters. In 1916 the Admiralty approved the gradual increase in female nurses to free up Sick Berth Attendants (SBAs) for service at sea. The Second World War again saw an increase in Reserve Sisters serving in Haslar which, together with members of the Voluntary Aid Detachment (VAD), filled the gaps left by the deployment of the regular Sisters and SBAs. Following the war VADs continued to work in Haslar and in 1949 SBAs of the Women's Royal Naval Service (WRNS) were being trained. In 1960 the VADs and Wren SBAs were replaced by QARNNS Naval Nursing Auxiliaries (NNA). Until this time the Naval Nursing Service had been an all-officer service. In 1962 nurse training for the State Registered Nurse (SRN) and State Enrolled Nurse (SEN) qualification commenced.

Patients in Haslar were now being nursed by QARNNS Sisters and Staff Nurses together with Student (SRN) and Pupil Nurses (SEN) under training as well as Royal Navy male trained nurses (Medical Technicians (Nursing) from 1965) and those under training, and RN Medical Assistants (MAs) (formerly SBAs) trained and under training. The School of Nursing was part of the Royal Naval Medical Staff School situated in *Dolphin II* but moved in 1987 to the former Sick Officers Block. Trained QARNNS personnel were also undertaking post-basic qualifications, so continuing the highest possible professional care for patients in Haslar.

On 1 April 1983 QARNNS became a Unified Nursing Service and male nursing colleagues in the Royal Navy were in future to join QARNNS. With shortages of Naval Nurses in Haslar, due partly to the ending of the SEN qualification, QARNNS Medical Assistant Branch was formed in 1987, and civilian nurses were briefly employed to ensure the safe and high standards of care continued for patients in Haslar. QARNNS MAs transferred to the Royal Navy in 1998. QARNNS Nursing Officers and Nurses continued to provide professional patient care, alongside their Army and Royal Air Force colleagues, from 1996 to 2009 in the Royal Hospital Haslar.

158 *QARNNS Sisters look out from the Sentry Post following a Rose Bowl Tennis Tournament.*

159 *QARNNS Sisters playing in the Franklin Tennis Tournament, 1959. In 1949 Miss Olga Franklin presented to QARNNS the Rose Bowl for presentation to the winner of an annual tennis tournament. Miss Franklin and two other QARNNS Sisters spent three years as prisoners of war of the Japanese at the Civilian Internment Camp at Stanley on Hong Kong Island. They were the only Sisters of QARNNS to live under enemy rule during the war.*

160 *QARNNS Nurses outside F Block (formerly D Block) in the early 1960s, when the block provided Nurses Quarters.*

161 *Stirring the Christmas pudding, early 1960s. SRA E. Bradbury RN, MOIC, Miss C. Thompson QARNNS Principal Matron, Miss M. Fetherston-Dilke Matron-in-Chief QARNNS.*

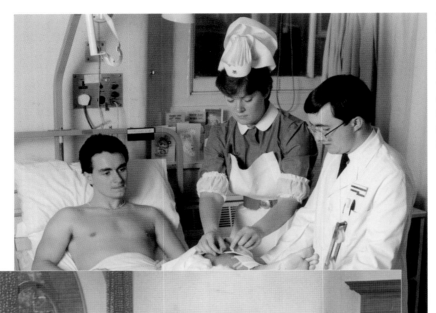

162 *Nurse Clinical Teacher with a Student Nurse on an Orthopaedic Ward, 1985. Student and Pupil Nurses gained their practical clinical experience in the wards of RNH Haslar.*

163 *QARNNS and RN Student Nurses in the Medical Library at RNH Haslar, 1962. Nurses in training undertook their formal education in the Training Division accommodation in* Dolphin II *and in June 1987 moved to the converted Officers Block which became The Royal Naval Medical Staff School.*

164 *QARNNS and RN Nurses in class in the Training Division, with Superintending Nursing Sister C. Cooke QARNNS Nurse Tutor. Nurse training began at RNH Haslar and RNH Plymouth in May 1962. In 1966 the title of Auxiliary Naval Nurse gave way to that of Naval Nurse.*

165 *HRH Princess Alexandra, QARNNS Patron since 1955, outside the Sisters' Mess with C. Thompson, Principal Matron QARNNS, and Naval Nurse Hill in 1969.*

166 *A QARNNS Nurse tending a patient at night, late 1980s.*

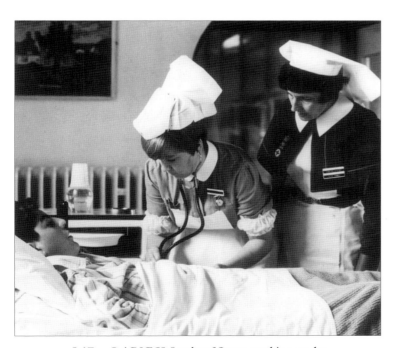

167 *QARNNS Student Nurses working under supervision in the Urology Ward. Senior Nursing Sister K. Funnell QARNNS was formerly a Wren SBA who transferred to QARNNS for nurse training, and was the first QARNNS Rating to become a QARNNS Nursing Sister.*

168 *QARNNS Medical Assistant in front of the hospital in 1989. Female Medical Assistants served in QARNNS on their inception in 1987 and were fully integrated into the RN Medical Branch in 1999.*

VADs (by Mrs Sylvia Bell)

In 1909 it was decided to form a Voluntary Aid Detachment to provide medical assistance in time of war. Volunteers were drawn from the Red Cross, St John's and St Andrew's. When the WRNS were formed in 1917, VADs were also invited to opt for service with the Royal Navy and the VAD (RN) came into being. They became part of the Reserved Forces of the Crown and mobile members were committed to serve anywhere: at home, on ships or in naval establishments overseas. At the outbreak of war in 1939 there were some 5,000 members enlisted in the VAD (RN) and most served at least part of their time in Haslar before going on to serve in other theatres of war, some even going to sea on carriers to transfer prisoners of war from the Far East to Australia and Canada.

VADs came from all walks of life. They bought their own uniforms both for nursing and for 'walking out'. Financial reward was minimal at £10 a month – less a sizeable deduction for messing but plus a small allowance for the upkeep of their uniforms.

The majority of VADs were employed as ward nurses, but others covered a wide range of duties including X-ray, operating theatre, dental assistant, laboratory technician, blood bank, pharmacist, medical secretary, clerks and cooks, and where necessary additional training was provided by the Navy.

While on duty each VAD took orders from her immediate superior, usually a QARRNS sister, but all were presided over by a Red Cross Commandant. Throughout the war this post was filled at Haslar by Miss Irene Waistall. She was a strict disciplinarian (she needed to be!) but always had the welfare of her VADs in mind and was highly respected.

VADs were accommodated in M Block (Zymotics) with any 'overspill' allocated to billets, mostly in Alverstoke about a mile away. Those living outside the hospital were issued with naval bicycles to facilitate their journeys to and from work at all hours of the day and night. These were heavy machines with fixed wheels, spiked pedals and hooded lights (for the blackout) and not easily managed, especially over Pneumonia Bridge!

Life in hospital could be very rewarding but also extremely tiring and, at times, intensely distressing. Most of the patients were young men, many with horrendous wounds, and not all survived. It was essential that VADs could enjoy some degree of recreation and the dances and shows in the Errol Hall were very popular. On one memorable occasion, Bud Flanagan gave a show to mark his appreciation of the way the hospital had cared for his son. For anyone lucky enough to obtain a late pass until 11pm, Gosport and Portsmouth offered wider scope for entertainment but such excursions usually involved walking 'home' in the blackout.

No doubt each VAD carried back to civilian life memories of one or more special incidents which had affected her deeply but all those present at the time will remember air-raid measures and the intense pressure following D-Day.

Although Portsmouth and Gosport were heavily bombed, Haslar Hospital escaped damage apart from one raid which hit the library and made a large hole in the 'quarter deck'. However, air-raid warnings were not infrequent and these required all patients – other than those who could not be moved for medical reasons – to be transported from the wards to the cellars where they remained with appropriate nursing staff until the 'all clear' was sounded.

So far as D-Day was concerned, staff were confined to the hospital before the event and, if possible, patients were moved to other hospitals to make room for the expected heavy intake of wounded personnel. The foreseen rush began on 7 June and there was no respite for many weeks. The patients were from all three British Services, from the allies and even from the German forces. The scale of the operation was awesome and, for many, brought home the dreadful human cost of war.

When they were able to find a brief respite from the wards, many VADs found solace in St Luke's Church. The organist would often play soothing music and one could pray for the patients and ask for strength to carry on, however tired one felt. It was with deep gratitude that a number of ex-VADs attended the last service at St Luke's in 2007.

VADs at Haslar felt specially privileged and the experience of serving there was unforgettable. The architecture was impressive; the history was remarkable – where else could one nurse in a ward once used by the wounded from Trafalgar? – and the location was wonderful. The Navy's premier base was just across the harbour and there were views of the Solent where naval activities seemed unceasing. The VADs were engulfed in the Senior Service and proud to be part of it.

VADs continued to serve with the Royal Navy until 1960 when they were disbanded. An Association was formed, with Lady Mountbatten of Burma as its patron. The Association held its inaugural meeting at Haslar and its final meeting at the Institute of Naval Medicine in Alverstoke, thereby enabling members to visit Haslar for conducted tours of the updated facilities and some of the wartime features, such as the underground operating theatres. What memories were evoked, some sad, some joyful, but all unforgettable!

169 *VADs in an operating theatre, preparing instrument trays and surgical apparatus in the 1940s.*

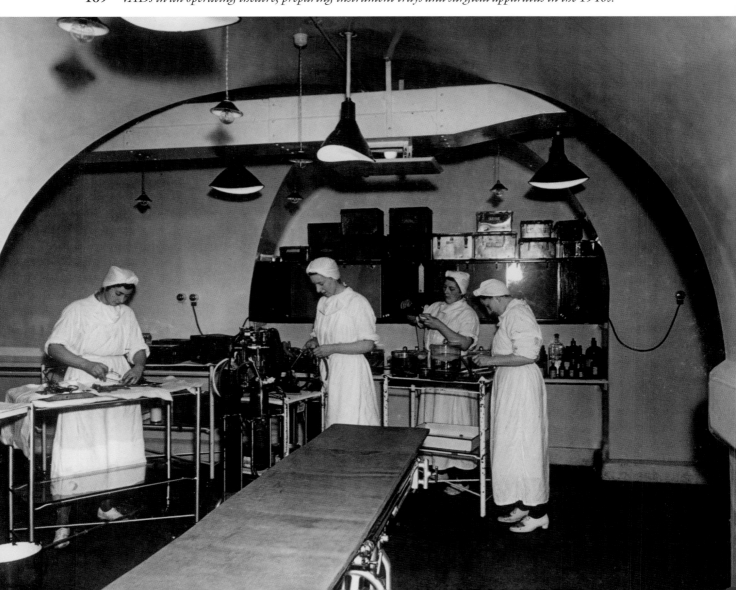

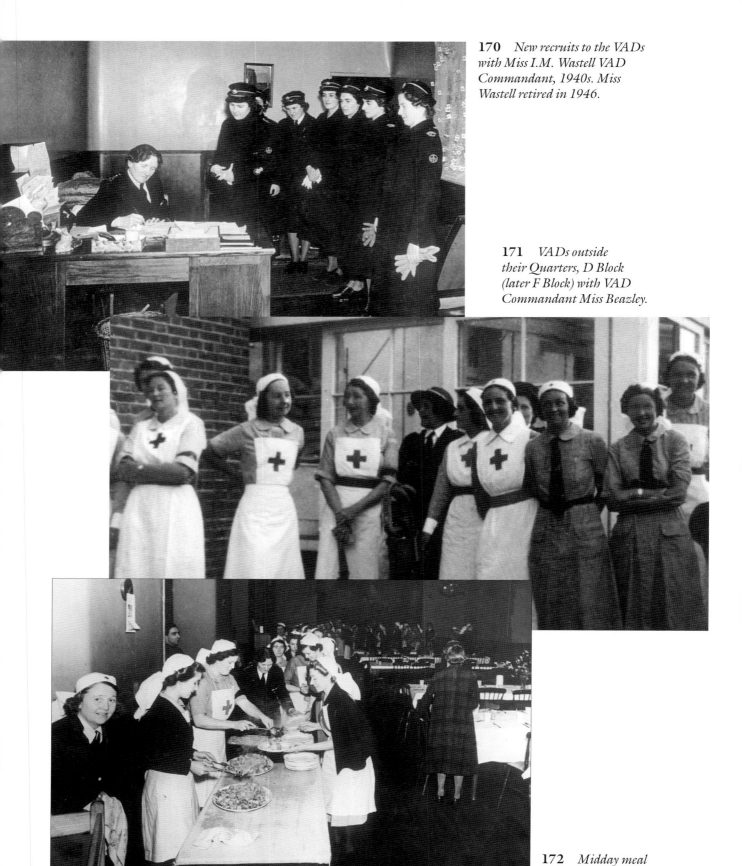

170 *New recruits to the VADs with Miss I.M. Wastell VAD Commandant, 1940s. Miss Wastell retired in 1946.*

171 *VADs outside their Quarters, D Block (later F Block) with VAD Commandant Miss Beazley.*

172 *Midday meal for the VADs.*

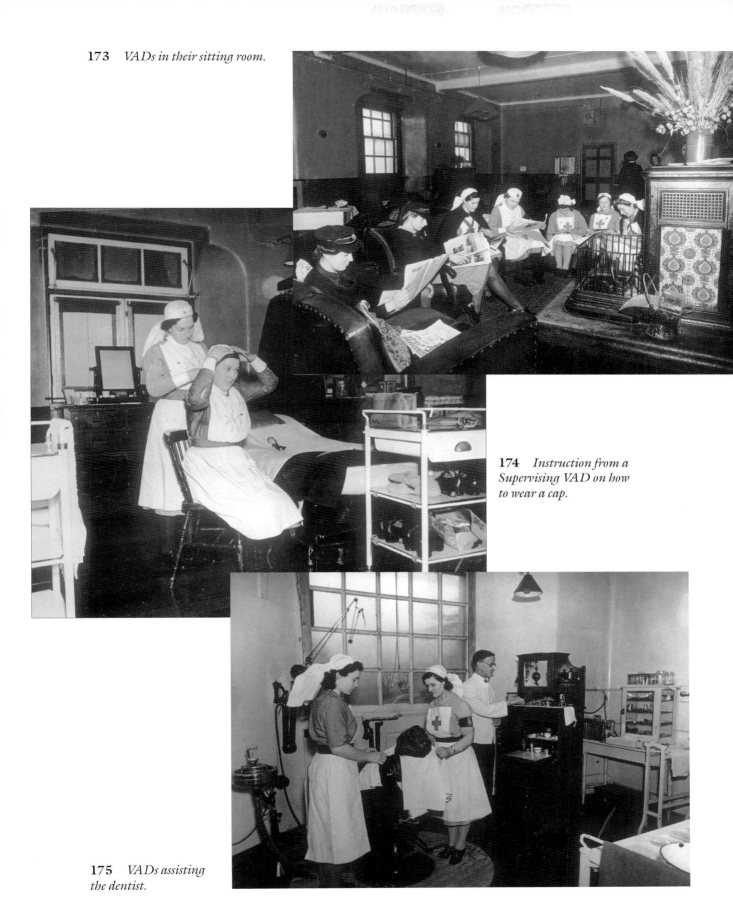

173 *VADs in their sitting room.*

174 *Instruction from a Supervising VAD on how to wear a cap.*

175 *VADs assisting the dentist.*

ROYAL HOSPITAL HASLAR

176 *QARNNS Nursing Officers and ratings on the balcony of Building 80, formerly Officers Block and later the Royal Naval Medical Staff School in 1999. In 1995 QARNNS Officers adopted Naval titles and rank insignia. The crossed As, the insignia of Queen Alexandra, has been retained as part of QARNNS uniform.*

ROYAL VISITS

In August 1855 Queen Victoria and Prince Albert visited the hospital. The Queen spent an hour touring the hospital, commenting favourably on the views of the Solent and the Isle of Wight.

A second visit 27 years later came close to being cancelled due to fog in the Solent. As the weather improved, the Queen arrived with little notice and presented campaign medals to those recently returned from Egypt. A young sailor called MacGuire who had lost a leg in action made to rise from his bed to meet the Queen but she gently placed her hand on his head and with a regal but motherly smile made him lay back on his pillow, and then pinned his medal to his bed jacket. Following this visit the Queen commented, 'Haslar Hospital was unquestionably the noblest of institutions of the kind in the Kingdom.' After the Queen's death Haslar was mentioned in her memorial published in the press: 'Haslar hospital testifies to her [the Queen's] loving thoughts for her seamen, for its wards and by her kind words and beneficent actions the Queen eased the pain of the sick and wounded from her ships.'

The future King George V, then the Duke of York, visited Haslar in March 1897 to speak to members of the Benin expedition. and he also toured the hospital and took lunch with the officers, with some of whom he had served whilst in the Navy. The King and Queen Mary returned in 1910.

On 9 May 1917 Queen Mary attended Haslar to open the newly built Canada Block and to tour the hospital, meeting both staff and patients and finally presenting service awards, amongst others, to those Royal Marines who had been awarded the Military Medal.

177   *Queen Victoria presents Commander Purvis with the Egypt Medal during her visit to RH Haslar on 23 December 1882.*

Queen Mary's daughter, Princess Mary the Princess Royal, visited Haslar in January 1943 as part of a visit to Portsmouth and was presented to QARNNS, VAD and Sick Berth staff and also took time to tour the hospital.

After the Second World War, Princess Alexandra visited Haslar on many occasions as Patron of Queen Alexandra's Royal Naval Nursing Service.

Lord Mountbatten was a regular visitor. His powder-blue Jaguar, with Naval Signalman radiator mount, would be parked in front of the Arcade and became a familiar sight. Staff who had the pleasure of meeting him were often struck by his ability to remember their names.

In 1982 the Prince of Wales visited those injured in the Falklands Campaign. He toured wards and departments, taking time to chat with both staff and patients, and on leaving through the Arcade stopped and chatted with staff and families.

178 *Queen Mary attended Haslar to open Canada Block on 9 May 1917 and, following the opening ceremony, she walked through the hospital and in front of the Arcade she presented Distinguished Service Medals to sailors and the Military Medal to two Royal Marines.*

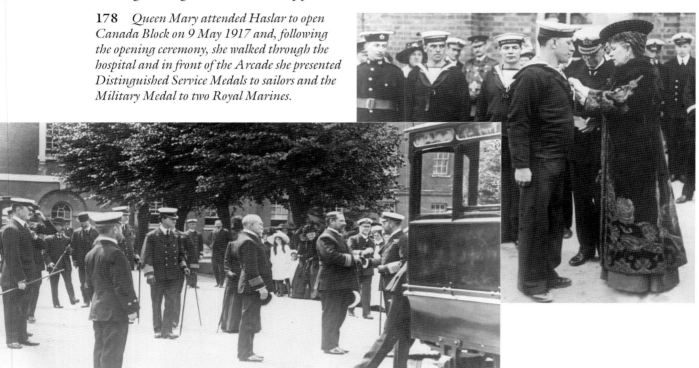

179 *A summer's day and everyone is well dressed to greet King George V on an official visit to RH Haslar. He arrived in a hospital tram. There is a spare tram in the siding, whilst a Sick Berth Branch Chief looks on with many hospital officers and civil staff in attendance. A QARNNS Nursing Sister can be seen in the crowd by the King's right shoulder. A group of hospital Sick Berth Staff wait in the Arcade.*

180 *King George V and Queen Mary alight from a hospital tram, 23 July 1910. All present are wearing Cowes Rig, white trousers and uniform jackets, the tradition when the Royal Family were at Cowes on the Royal Yacht Victoria and Albert. During their tour of the hospital they visited the wards, St Luke's Church and the Operating Theatre situated over the Arcade.*

181 *VADs are presented to Princess Mary, the Princess Royal, during her visit to Haslar in January 1943.*

182 *Princess Mary passes C (previously F) Block whilst talking with a QARNNS Sister and accompanied by Surgeon Rear Admiral Eric Bradbury. Commandant Wastell VAD walks behind.*

183 *Princess Alexandra, Patron QARNNS, meets Naval Nursing Auxiliaries during a visit to Haslar.*

184   *The Prince of Wales arrives in the Arcade in 1982 and is greeted by Miss Wade, Matron, and Surgeon Rear Admiral Houghton before visiting patients from the Falklands Campaign.*

185   *The Prince of Wales with QARNNS Senior Nursing Sister Christina Arnold and John Strange, an injured crew member from HMS Sheffield. John had been repatriated from the Falklands onboard the Hospital Ship* Uganda.

186   *Surgeon Captain John Richardson, Medical Officer in Charge at Haslar, leads the Prince of Wales through a ward accompanied by Senior Nursing Officer Arnold.*

HASLAR 250

The Haslar Heritage Group was formed in 2001 to plan events to mark the hospital's 250th birthday in 2003. The events were spread throughout the year although this was not the original intention. It became necessary as many of the hospital staff spent some months in Kuwait and Iraq.

In June 2003 the BBC Antiques Roadshow visited, with well-known stalwarts including Michael Aspel and Henry Sandon. A few days later a visit by former QARNNS and VAD Nurses allowed the Heritage Group to gather information to complete the boards hung in the main corridor of the Crosslink building. The display boards ultimately provided the idea to produce this book.

187   *Michael Aspel discusses Arms and Militaria with expert Bill Harriman, whilst an attentive audience looks on.*

188   *Having taken a break from discussing his favourite subject, 'Pots', Henry Sandon has his pulse taken by Lt Fletcher QARNNS. No doubt it had been raised by the sight of so many Nurses, dressed in their ward uniform, acting as Stewards for the day.*

189   On a perfect June day Michael Aspel pulls a pint of 'Haslar Celebration Ale' in the beer tent, watched by Lt Col Phil Ward and Eric Birbeck, with Dave Pickersgill of Oakleaf Brewery who brewed the special edition ale. The label carried the story of beer issue to patients at Haslar.

190   The public wait in orderly line to present their antiques to a specialist. The queues continued until late afternoon.

191   Hospital staff, families and friends enjoy stirring music by the Band of HM Royal Marines, Portsmouth at Proms in the Park with Haslar as the backdrop. The evening started with the roar of a Merlin engine as a Spitfire soared overhead.

192   As with all Proms in the Park, patriotic music and fireworks brought a splendid summer's evening to a close.

An Historical Meeting and Dinner was held in May 2004, with many past Commanding Officers and Matrons attending. The atmosphere of the day is best conveyed by the speech made by Surgeon Captain Ray Radford CBE, a former Medical Officer in Charge of Haslar:

7 May 2004

Mr President, Distinguished Guests, Ladies and Gentlemen.

What a marvellous day we have had and most of us present have sufficient experience to know that it does not happen by magic. We thank again today's presenters, they must have spent many hours honing their talks to reach the superb level that they achieved and we thank MDG for his courtesy in hosting us for lunch. I regret that in his otherwise superb talk Commander Jeff Tall reminded us that you join Haslar by Pneumonia Bridge and leave by Dead Man's Mile.

I must point out that due to increased efficiency and moving the main gate it is now only three-quarters of a mile. It is a privilege to have been invited today and our thanks go to the Haslar 250 Committee and in particular to that indefatigable group, Col Phil Ward and Mr Eric Birbeck and not forgetting Mrs Ann Ryder as well, who have all contributed so much, not only to today, but to the whole year's memorable functions.

We are dining in a historic mess and, by the way we have been looked after, the standards traditional to the Submarine Service and to the Haslar Medical Mess are in good hands and are being well maintained. The front of the menu stimulates me to ask a favour of Eric, namely that he will convey to the department of Medical Illustration the delight that their beautiful art works, in so many formats, have given during the year. They are a joy to look at.

We will shortly be toasting 250 years of Service by Haslar to the Armed Forces, the civilian population of Gosport and, by its research and training, to British Medicine in general. Haslar's name has permanently entered national history and national vocabulary and for my part I am specially honoured to have been asked to propose the toast in such distinguished company. (I hope there are no people here so mean minded as to be hoping that I will slip up over the hospital's name or for that matter the name of Fort Blockhouse.)

What do we mean by Haslar? A fine building. They built well in those days and I do not need to remind one certain person here tonight that only diamond drills could persuade it to be connected to the Crosslink. The walls may have been rigid but Haslar has been just the opposite. Over its 250 years it has been noted for its flexibility, constantly adjusting itself both architecturally and functionally to the demands of the Service in Peace and War, keeping in the forefront of Medical advances, giving its patients the care and treatment they rightly deserved and, last but not least, launching on their lifetime careers, generations of Nurses, Doctors in Specialist disciplines, Technicians, Medical Branch Personnel, Radiographers, Physiotherapists and Civil Staff, along with many others.

In a way the most dramatic developments have taken place in the last fifty or so years and many of the people here tonight experienced them, or even instigated them. We have seen Haslar change from a post-war, half-day, sleepy hollow to a first-class comprehensive District General Hospital for the Navy and Gosport Population and then to a Triservice Hospital and base.

Whatever turf wars took place in the higher Single Service ranks, the young soldiers, sailors and airmen at the workface put them to shame, with no loss of their own service's identity by their concentration on the task in hand and their friendly relations both in the hospital and on deployment. The Haslar-based esprit-de-corps was summed up by a notice I saw in the Theatre coffee room. It read, 'Thursday, Army Run Ashore'.

I have mentioned the civilian population specially, because they have always supported Haslar and Haslar has always supported them. Certainly a gratifying feature in the recent years of uncertainty has been the resounding toast to Haslar sounded by the civilian population in its tireless efforts to save it.

Many here are ex-Matrons and MOICs, and one thing you quickly learn is that there is more to a hospital than Doctors and Nurses. How humbling it is, on taking charge, to visit areas that you have hardly entered before and have taken for granted – stores, kitchens, workshops, offices, greenhouses, boiler rooms, CSSD, laundry (notice padre, I didn't say the church) – and find them staffed by desperately loyal, unassuming people who have given their working lives to Haslar, serving totally out of the limelight. Their predecessors, often quaintly and intriguingly titled, have run through its 250 years of history and we will not forget them all when we toast the hospital.

Perhaps for Freudian reasons, because I cannot totally believe it will ever happen, I have skated around the threat of closure, but we all know that the final step in the reorganisation of the Defence Medical Services, financially and administratively, is planned to be the closure in a few years time of Haslar as a military unit. It is poignant at a time when Haslar still runs nine, arguably ten, operating theatres and even more Army and Navy Units are moving to Gosport. We do recognise that the decision was not taken lightly but it still grieves us greatly. It is no consolation to be following the path of the other great service hospitals such as Woolwich, Wroughton, The Cambridge at Aldershot, Plymouth, or, for that matter, of many famous civilian hospitals. We all hope that if Haslar ceases to be a Service establishment its facilities will be retained in some form by the NHS. And even more, that its historic name will be perpetuated in some way.

What is also important is that before Haslar fully closes, freely available, high quality, local hospital services are guaranteed for the many servicemen and families based in this area on a long- or possibly even more important, short-term basis. The planning and negotiating required places a great burden on those responsible, not least the Surgeon General, Surgeon Vice Admiral Ian Jenkins, and the new CO, Surgeon Captain James Campbell. We would like to express our confidence in their wisdom and judgement and to extend to James our congratulations and best wishes on his joining the prestigious list of people who have had the honour of leading this great establishment over 250 years.

I come now to the toast itself. I shall be asking you to rise and drink a toast to this great historic hospital, to all that it has achieved and to all, great and small, who served it over 250 years. Please rise, Ladies and Gentlemen, to toast:

THE ROYAL HOSPITAL HASLAR.

Happy Christmas

Christmas in hospital was always a special time. Many patients would be given home sick leave but staff did their best to ensure that the patients remaining enjoyed the festive season as much as they were able. On Christmas Day visits might come from Santa, with presents, the Surgeon Rear Admiral in Charge, Matron and the Mayor. Wards were decorated and carol services were held in St Luke's. Staff would also sing carols around the wards. In the late 1940s and the 1950s lights were strung between the trees in front of the Arcade. A large Christmas star was placed on the bell cupola of St Luke's until 2006.

The war years were no exception and staff did their best to carry on the Christmas tradition. Despite rationing, the food was good and one VAD, who served at Haslar at the time, remembers how VAD Commandant Wastell 'grasped things out of Heaven' in order to ensure that staff had special treats. A special treat for 'Jack' was a beer ration, not just at Christmas but on a daily basis, Doctor's orders permitting. Stacks of Brickwoods Brewery crates could always be seen at the entrance to Victualling Office store, delivered daily. Officers were permitted wine and spirits.

193 *The snow lies deep, crisp and even in the winter of 1954 and there is not a footprint to be seen. The pollarded trees of Admiral's Walk stand like sentinels across the hospital quadrangle.*

194 *An Edwardian Christmas. QARNNS Nursing Sisters, Sick Berth Staff and patients await a visit from Inspector General of Hospitals and Fleets, T.D. Gimlette CB. The 'Hearty Welcome' sign on the wall behind the ward stove has been made from cotton wool and no doubt the Christmas decorations were also hand-made by the patients. It appears that the patients await lunch, and perhaps the Inspector to carve the turkey?*

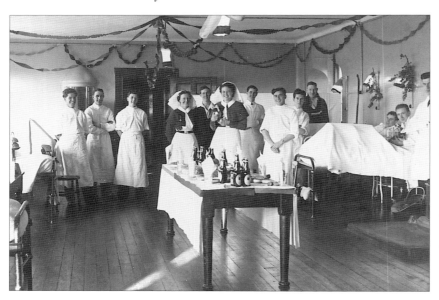

195 *The coal scuttle stands full by the ward fire in this festive picture and again QARNNS Nursing Sisters and Sick Berth Staff pose for the camera with patients who were to spend Christmas in hospital. The table is laden with bottled beer, dates, nuts and crackers. This picture shows the teak floor of the ward. Once a week the beds were pushed back so that the Nurses and Sick Berth Staff could lay down tea leaves and sweep through collecting the dust.*

196   *Christmas 1949 and Sister Joyce Cattermole, Dr Crouch, L/SBA Bannister and SBA Packham and other staff and patients pose for J.C. Lawrence, the well-known Gosport photographer.*

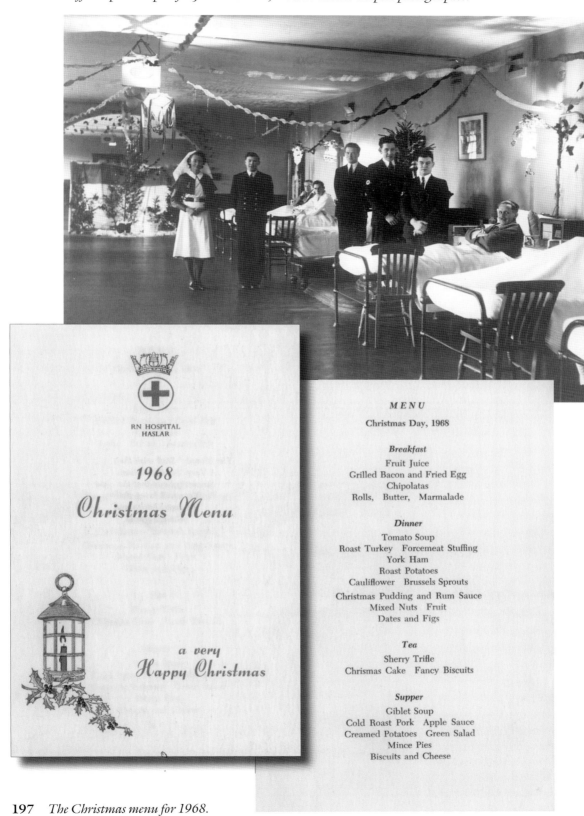

RN HOSPITAL
HASLAR

1968

Christmas Menu

a very
Happy Christmas

MENU
Christmas Day, 1968

Breakfast
Fruit Juice
Grilled Bacon and Fried Egg
Chipolatas
Rolls,   Butter,   Marmalade

Dinner
Tomato Soup
Roast Turkey   Forcemeat Stuffing
York Ham
Roast Potatoes
Cauliflower   Brussels Sprouts
Christmas Pudding and Rum Sauce
Mixed Nuts   Fruit
Dates and Figs

Tea
Sherry Trifle
Chrismas Cake   Fancy Biscuits

Supper
Giblet Soup
Cold Roast Pork   Apple Sauce
Creamed Potatoes   Green Salad
Mince Pies
Biscuits and Cheese

197   *The Christmas menu for 1968.*

198 *This simple and evocative line drawn card by E.G. Tucker portrays the life of the VADs in Haslar during 1943. Warships and the forts in the Solent, Portsmouth and a small ferry are on the left with the front of Haslar on the right. In the centre, QARNNs, VADs and Sick Berth Staff go about their duties with the Admiral's Walk and St Luke's in the background. At the centre left, the VADs enjoy Christmas lunch in their mess, cats and all. Centre right, a dormitory scene shows VADS unpacking and fixing their uniform and hats with stockings drying on hangers at the end of the beds. The emblems at the bottom of the card are for the Red Cross, VADs and St John's.*

In reality, the life of all staff at Haslar during the war meant hard work caring for the injured. Staff often worked long 12-hour shifts with short six-hour breaks.

199 *A Christmas card from 1943 depicting a VAD and St John's Nurse looking down on Haslar with warships in the Solent beyond and Portsmouth on the left. Even the hospital water tower features in this card.*

CHRISTMAS 1943 GREETINGS

Burials, Excavations and Memorials

Much of the land to the south-west of the hospital was used for burials. This includes the area now known as the 'Paddock', on which The Terrace was built and the Memorial Garden. The number of burials in Haslar is likely to amount to tens of thousands but it is difficult to establish an exact figure. During the years 1779-80, James Lind reported 1,716 deaths and burials in the hospital. In 1782, following the capsize of the *Royal George* at Spithead, 600 sailors, possibly including Admiral Kempenfelt, were interred at Haslar.

During the Napoleonic Wars Haslar was busy, not just with Naval patients but also with Army patients, especially after the closure of the Army General Hospital in Gosport which had a brief life on the site of what is now St Vincent College. In the years 1808 and 1809 there were 1,256 burials. A significant number of these were soldiers of Sir John Moore's Army who were admitted suffering from typhus and dysentery following the retreat from Corunna. Others were sailors, soldiers with Walcheren fever, Russian sailors whose ships had been impounded, and some hospital staff.

Records from 1825 show that grave robbers were active in the grounds of Haslar. Three were caught and sentenced to imprisonment at the Lentern Assizes held at Winchester. In 1826 the north corner of the paddock was enclosed. Headstones from other parts of the paddock were moved to line the wall of this area. During the next 33 years it was used for burials. Many staff and their families were interred here, including Lieutenant Alexander Forsyth Parr who, following service with Nelson at the battles of the Nile, Trafalgar and Copenhagen, was Lieutenant of the hospital for 25 years. Among the patients buried here are a sailor from the USS *Niagara* and a sailor from HMY *Victoria and Albert*. This burial area is now known as the Memorial Garden.

From 1859 burials continued at the newly established Naval Cemetery in Clayhall Road. Funeral processions started from the hospital, continued along Haslar Road and then into Clayhall Road. The route became known as 'Dead Man's Mile'. Bands playing funeral marches were asked not to strike up until some distance from the hospital.

In 2005 the first formal archaeological dig was undertaken in the Paddock area, resulting in interesting finds, and further digs were carried out in subsequent years as a joint MoD, Defence Estates, Cranfield University project. Results have shown that bodies were interred sequentially, with one grave dug, the body buried, and then the next grave dug. The bodies were found to be aligned northwest-southeast, whereas east-west is more usual. It is possible that space was a constraint, or that the burials were aligned with the main hospital axis. Over the period of excavation coffin nails

200   *The Haslar Paddock looking towards the Terrace. From 1753 until 1826 this was the main burial area.*

were found along with surviving wood from coffins (pine). Records show that funerals cost seven shillings and sixpence, but many people could not meet the cost from their meagre estate. Sometimes it was met by friends or from the sale of the deceased's belongings (a naval custom). A number of skeletons were removed for further analysis and all of these are likely to be male and under 35 years of age, with two being assessed as under 20 years of age.

The Haslar Heritage Group noted that many graves were unmarked and arranged for a memorial plaque to be unveiled and dedicated to all who served their country and ended their days at Haslar and were buried in the hospital. On 10 June 2005 Admiral Sir Alan West GCB, DSC, ADC, First Sea Lord, unveiled the memorial plaque.

201   *The Paddock looking towards Clayhall. In the foreground is an area recently excavated. Until 1826 headstones marked burials in these grounds but they were later transferred into what is now the Memorial Garden, which served the hospital from 1826 to 1859 when Clayhall Naval Cemetery opened.*

202   *A view from the top floor of the Surgeon Rear Admiral's Residence showing the Paddock and the gardens to the rear of the Terrace. Bodies were also buried in the area now occupied by the walled gardens. Top left is the old HM Detention Centre, previously a Borstal, which in the 19th century had been an Army hospital and camp for the troops returning from the retreat from Corunna in 1809.*

203   *Excavation of the Paddock area was first undertaken in 2005. This picture shows Surgeon Captain Campbell, Lt Col Jones and Mrs Frances Allan viewing an excavated grave with the archaeologist.*

204 *This is the grave seen in the previous picture, showing three skeletons with excavation markers in place. It was believed that they were buried in hammocks but excavation has revealed that bodies were often buried in pine coffins. Over time, the coffins collapsed within the grave.*

205 *Modern forensic archaeology has allowed archaeologists to take tooth enamel samples in order to find out where the person was born and lived.*

206 *The Memorial Garden. A peaceful and tranquil area with many hospital staff buried alongside patients of the hospital from 1826 to 1859. Sir John Richardson's first wife and son Kendal were buried here. Some trees within the garden are dedicated to personnel who served both at Haslar and in the Naval Medical Services and whose ashes are scattered in the gardens.*

207 *10 June 2005. Admiral Sir Alan West GCB, DSC, ADC, First Sea Lord, admires the Plaque unveiled to commemorate those who served their country in both the Navy and Army and who died from wounds and disease and were buried in the Paddock with no marked grave.*

208 *In Memoriam. The Plaque and ceremony were paid for by the Haslar Heritage Group.*

Royal Hospital Haslar Burial Ground
In Memoriam

From 1753 until 1826 the area beyond this wall, known as the Paddock was used as a burial ground to lay to rest many thousands of sick and wounded who ended their days in Haslar Hospital. Amongst those interred here are soldiers and sailors who gave their lives for their country during the turbulent days of Trafalgar, Corunna and Waterloo. They lie side by side, Hammocks their shrouds and coffins, brothers in arms in death as in life.

This plaque was unveiled by
Admiral Sir Alan West GCB, DSC, ADC
First Sea Lord
10 June 2005

209 *Members of the Queen Alexandra's Royal Naval Nursing Service and Queen Alexandra's Royal Army Nursing Service stand heads bowed ready to lay the wreaths.*

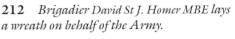

212   *Brigadier David St J. Homer MBE lays a wreath on behalf of the Army.*

210   *Admiral Sir Alan West lays a wreath on behalf of the Royal Navy.*

211   *Surgeon Captain J. Campbell lays a wreath on behalf of the Royal Hospital Haslar.*

213   *Admiral Sir Alan West with Ann Ryder, Eric Birbeck and Lt Col Ward RAMC, the Haslar Heritage Group.*

In memory of those members of our former regiments interred here, who lost their lives in the service of their country, establishing the traditions which are still upheld today, and whose exploits have served as an inspiration to subsequent generations.

214   *Admiral Sir Alan West poses with past and present members of Queen Alexandra's Royal Naval Nursing Service and Mrs Sylvia Bell of the Voluntary Aid Detachment that served at Haslar during the Second World War.*

92

215 *The First World War Memorial to Medical Officers and QARNNS Nursing Staff who lost their lives during the war is dedicated on Thursday 17 August 1922 with Surgeon Rear Admiral W. Bett CB, MVO, Medical Officer in Charge of Haslar, in attendance.*

216 *The War Memorial dedicated to members of the Sick Berth Branch and Sick Berth Reserve who gave their lives in both World Wars. This memorial was initially placed in the area between Canada Block and G block, then moved to face Canada Block and finally to the front of Haslar.*

IN MEMORY OF
THE SICK BERTH STAFF
AND
AUXILLARY SICK BERTH
RESERVE
OF THIS PORT
WHO LOST THEIR LIVES
DURING THE 2ND GREAT WAR
1939 – 1945

217 *Dr Andrew Shortland of Cranfield University, Bedford and Phil Harding of* Time Team *discuss the archaeological excavation for a documentary broadcast in 2009.*

218 *Students from Cranfield Forensic Institute prepare to lift a skeleton for achaeological research.*

219 Time Team *filming in the Paddock.*

GETTING TO HASLAR

Haslar has never been the simplest of places to get to. Those who served and worked at Haslar a few decades ago remember the PAS (Port Auxiliary Service) boats calling at numerous Naval Establishments on both sides of Portsmouth Harbour and at the Haslar Jetty. Alternatively, the Gosport Provincial Bus Company's No. 11 bus could be taken from near the ferry in Gosport via Alverstoke, down 'Dead Man's Mile' to the gates of the hospital, before turning on the sea-wall at the gates of HMS *Dolphin*.

When the hospital opened the principal access was by boat to Haslar Jetty. Some of those travelling to and from ships at Spithead landed on the Haslar foreshore. In the 18th century, a doctor from the hospital tasked with visiting the sick floating at Spithead complained that his rower was repeatedly press ganged! Early access from Gosport was either a long journey by horse or carriage via Alverstoke, or via the ferry across Haslar Creek near where bridges were later built.

The ferryman was an employee of the hospital and was not pleased when a Mr Forbes built the first bridge across Haslar Creek in 1795. The ferryman built a house on the Gosport side of the bridge and irritated the Governor and Council of the hospital by obtaining a licence to sell liquor at a time when drunkenness was a great problem in Haslar. The problem was solved in 1807 when the bridge was destroyed. The circumstances of the destruction are unclear.

A temporary timber footbridge built by the Royal Engineers in 1811 lasted until 1814 when it collapsed. In 1833 four men drowned while attempting to cross Haslar Creek during gales. This may have encouraged

220 *With the main gate open, two members of the Metropolitan Police are on duty and ready to receive an ambulance tram car from the Haslar Jetty. The main entrance had three gates, one to the right of the tramway gate that allowed people on foot to enter the hospital, the night bell having to be rung in the silent hours when the gate was closed. To the left of the centre gate was a larger gate for road traffic. It was not until 1984 that the new gate was put in place on the Haslar road in order to cope with larger vehicles.*

the construction of a road bridge in 1835. During the Second World War the centre of this bridge was removed to allow boats access to the Gun Boat yard. A steep pedestrian bridge was built over and across the gap which soon became known as 'Pneumonia Bridge'. Such was the height of the bridge that in winter, in a full-blown westerly or easterly gale, getting to Haslar was no fun at all!

Pneumonia Bridge holds many memories for Haslar staff, including late night walks back from Gosport and a last pint in the *Haslar Tavern* that stood opposite Trinity Church. Staff walked over the bridge late at night in the other direction on a duty run from the Juniors Mess with a 'Pussers Ditty Box' (small hand case) to collect an order of egg banjos (sandwiches) from the Cartoon Café in Squeeze Gut Alley (Bemisters Lane).

In 1877 a tramway was built from the Haslar Jetty through the main gate to the Arcade, where the patients receiving room was situated. Three tram cars were built by The Midland Railway Carriage and Wagon Company (Saltley). The cars were hand-propelled, a handrail being placed on either side of the car which was pushed by staff to and from the Jetty. There were points at each end of the tramway. King George V was just one important visitor propelled back and forth on his official visits to the hospital. An 18-inch gauge track also ran parallel, using the left-hand rail of the tram track up to the main gate of Haslar. It then veered left towards Fort Blockhouse (later HMS *Dolphin*). At the sea-wall the line also turned right and ran along the hospital sea front, allowing patients to be delivered to Zymotics (infectious diseases, Isolation) Hospital. It then continued past Fort Monkton and Gilkicker to the pier at Stokes Bay, allowing munitions, mines and torpedoes to be delivered from Blockhouse to ships in the Solent. Both the tramway and railway became derelict in the 1920s.

221 *A tram with patient is pushed into the hospital, 3 January 1907. This method was labour-intensive, hence the number of sailors in a variety of Naval rigs required for one tram. The patient's stretcher was mounted in the middle of the tram and this patient was from a fire at the Gunwharf (HMS* Vernon*).*

222 *The railhead at the front of Zymotic Hospital. Patients were entrained at the Haslar Jetty and taken on a short ride along the sea front and then admitted for what could be a lengthy stay of up to six months.*

223 *A remnant of track remaining in the Arcade. From the opening of the hospital until the late 20th century patients were unloaded here from handcarts, trams or ambulances.*

224 *Hospital staff leave Haslar Jetty on a PAS boat en route for either Portsmouth Station, HMS* Vernon, Kings Stairs *or HMS* Excellent. *Doctors, QARNNS Sisters and Wardmasters were allocated the comfort of the stern section, all other staff having to sit on the sides in all weathers. Submariners from HM Submarine* Grampus *look down from the conning tower.*

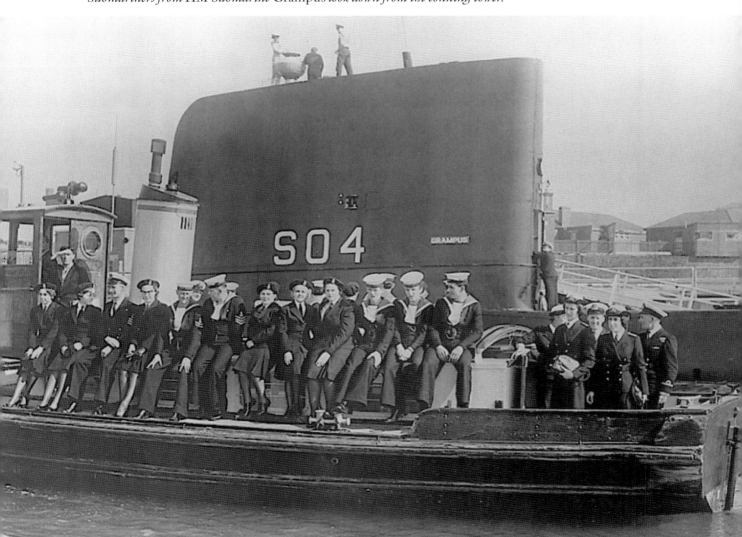

225 *Haslar from the Gosport foreshore, a fine picture believed to have been taken around 1880. Through the masts of the boats on the far side of the bridge can be seen the turrets of the Police Post that stood in front of the main gate of the hospital.*

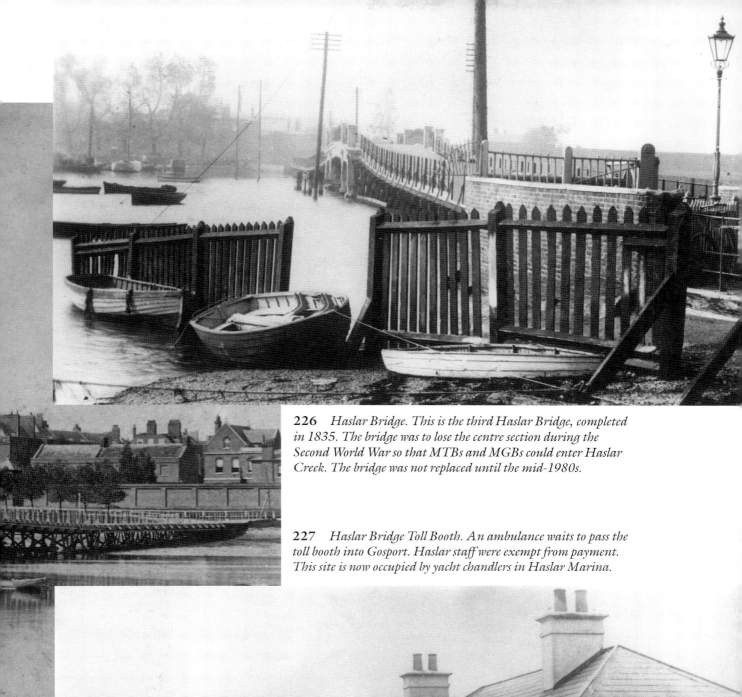

226 *Haslar Bridge. This is the third Haslar Bridge, completed in 1835. The bridge was to lose the centre section during the Second World War so that MTBs and MGBs could enter Haslar Creek. The bridge was not replaced until the mid-1980s.*

227 *Haslar Bridge Toll Booth. An ambulance waits to pass the toll booth into Gosport. Haslar staff were exempt from payment. This site is now occupied by yacht chandlers in Haslar Marina.*

229 *Pneumonia Bridge, c.1970s. This bridge was aptly named as in winter, with a westerly or easterly gale and rain, nobody got to the other side dry. The bridge was meant to be temporary but it stayed in place until the late 1970s. The original bridge can be seen below and was an ideal fishing point. On one occasion Sick Berth Staff from Haslar managed to get an Austin 7 across – some feat! Many staff tried to swim this point and at least one life was lost.*

230 *A hospital barge of 1866 with the Royal Victoria Hospital Netley in the background. This vessel was used to transfer patients from troop transports anchored in the Solent to either Haslar or Netley hospitals.*

Closure and Freedom Ceremonies

The number of sick in Gosport forced the opening of the hospital in October 1753, the main range being completed in 1754. The title Royal Naval Hospital Haslar was used informally at first, but became the formal title of the hospital in the 20th century.

Just two years after it became a Tri-Service hospital in 1996, the Commanding Officer of the now Royal Hospital Haslar, Brigadier Guy Ratcliffe, addressed the staff in St Luke's Church to inform them that Haslar was expected to close in 2001 or 2002. It continued as a military hospital until 2007, operated in partnership with the Portsmouth Hospitals NHS Trust, and then for a further two years remained in use by the NHS while the redevelopment of the Queen Alexandra Hospital at Cosham proceeded.

230 *After 242 years of continuous service as a Naval hospital the white ensign is lowered for the last time in April 1996. The Royal Naval Hospital Haslar transfers into a new era as a Tri-Service hospital including continuing service to the civilian population of the surrounding area.*

231   *The Band of HM Royal Marines, Portsmouth marches away from the handover ceremony with a Guard of Naval Medical Branch Staff, QARNNS, RAMC, QARANC and PMRAFNS lining the road.*

232   *The Royal Marines Band Plymouth stands ready to lead the Parade of Hospital Staff through the ceremonial gate to Gosport for the Freedom of Gosport Ceremony 29 March 2007. The first march of the parade was to 'Haslar Farewell', a march commissioned by the Haslar Heritage Group and composed by Captain Peter Curtis RM.*

233 *Royal Naval Medical Branch Staff and Queen Alexandra's Royal Naval Nursing Service led by Lt Jason Davies, Medical Services.*

234 *Royal Army Medical Corps, Queen Alexandra Royal Army Nursing Corps and Royal Army Dental Corps led by Captain Ian Treveil RAMC.*

235 *Royal Air Force Medical Staff and Princess Mary's Royal Air Force Nursing Service Staff led by Warrant Officer George Cuthbert RAF.*

236 *Royal Hospital Haslar MOD Civilian Staff march proudly with their service colleagues led by Mrs Ann Ryder.*

237   *The Standard of the Royal Naval Sick Berth and Medical Branch Association leads retired members of the Branch, many having trained and served at Haslar. Retired members of the QARNNS followed.*

238   *The RH Haslar Closure Ceremony, 30 March 2007. Surgeon Captain James Campbell, the outgoing Commanding Officer in Charge of RH Haslar, pauses to reflect with a member of the RN Medical Branch under the watchful eye of WO George Cuthbert.*

239   *The Union Flag lowered for the last time as part of the RH Haslar Closure Ceremony watched by both the media and Haslar Staff.*

240 *The well-known Naval hymn 'Eternal Father Strong to Save' rings out across a wet gathering. This was a different day weather-wise from the Freedom Ceremony held in bright spring sunlight the day before.*

241 *True to tradition, the Commanding Officer and his wife are about to be drawn out of the Hospital through the Haslar Ceremonial gate on a Gun Carriage pulled by hospital staff.*

242 *'How did we do?' asks Captain Campbell, watched by staff and Commander Ian Coulton, Officer Commanding Fort Blockhouse.*

243 *Queen Alexandra's Royal Naval Nursing Service Matrons and Sisters. From left to right: Commander Jean Bancroft, Miss Pamela Graystone RRC, Miss Pat Gould CBE RRC, Captain Julia Massey RRC, Captain Trish Hambling OBE, ARRC and Miss Eileen Northway CBE, RRC.*

244 *To the applause of gathered staff and friends, Mrs Frances Allan, Hospital Director, cuts the decommissioning cake with Surgeon Captain Campbell's Naval Sword.*

Royal Hospital Haslar Commanding Officer's Decommissioning Speech 30 March 2007

In a few short minutes we will haul down the flag for the last time, and the Royal Hospital Haslar will cease to be a military unit. It is an appropriate time to reflect and give thanks for all those who work here now and all those who went before us:

254 years
73 Commanding Officers and as many matrons
Thousands upon thousands of doctors
Tens of thousands of nurses, technicians and other essential military staff
An army of civilian workers
Millions of patients
A host of smiles and a river of tears, in equal numbers
Great triumphs and breakthroughs, plus a few disasters
A seat of teaching and learning
A home to many and a lifetime's work to others

Since this great institution first graced the skyline of Gosport in the 1750s, she has found a place in the hearts and memories of so many people. She has experienced times of fame and high praise, neglect at other times, bombing by the enemy; coveted jealously by some, mocked by others – but never ignored.

She was already a mature lady at the time of Trafalgar, took in the sick and wounded from Corunna, maintained the health of the Fleet during the Pax Britannica, shone during World War 1, excelled during World War 2 and D-Day, took in some of the wounded after their long journey home from the Falklands, now 25 years ago.

We are military medical people working in a fine medical institution. For us, it's all about the patients. We must be able to respond to their needs. We live in a changing world with different and challenging wounds of war. Our casualties now survive with complex multiple injuries which would, and do, tax the most advanced of hospitals. I myself have seen and treated these wounds in Iraq and the Afghan plains, where our wounded soldiers, sailors, marines and airmen and women get the top class treatment they deserve.

However, back here in the UK, we no longer see the survivors of a distant battle brought home after a long sea journey, which was the model that the Royal Hospital Haslar was built to serve. They now fly home swiftly and need immediate high level care from a legion of top specialists. Throughout her long history, the Royal Hospital Haslar has adapted to the demands placed upon her. We can no longer respond to these demands here.

The Royal Hospital Haslar was noble in concept, elegant in design and robust of build. She is the Alma Mater to generations and has been the salvation of many.

She was charged with providing help and succour
to the sick and wounded of the Fleet.
She has discharged her duty.
That is all.

Surgeon Captain J.K. Campbell Royal Navy

245   *Haslar, taken from the tramway.*

Royal Hospital Haslar Staff

Commanding Officers

The following is a list of Commanding Officers and other senior officers of the Royal Hospital Haslar from October 1753 to the hospital's closure in 2009. The listing has been taken from available information within Royal Hospital Haslar using name and title boards. The information has been transcribed directly from the title boards and apologies are offered if names are missing, or if errors have occurred. The fault lies with the sign writer who held the brush at the time and whose brush has long lain idle.

Physicians and Council

10 October 1753	George Cuthbert MD
1 June 1758	James Lind MD
	'Father of Naval Medicine'
24 June 1783	John Lind MD

Governors

26 August 1795	William Yeo Captain
	(Buried in the Paddock of RH Haslar)
1 July 1808	Charles Craven Captain

Superintendents

24 February 1820	H. Garrett Rear Admiral
5 April 1838	Sir E. Chetham Kt KCH Captain
2 December 1841	J. Carter Captain
2 December 1846	Sir W.E. Parry Kt FRS Captain
26 July 1852	W.J. Hope-Johnstone Captain
6 May 1853	G.W.C. Courtney Captain
14 December 1854	H. Smith CB Captain
10 July 1855	S.C. Dacres Captain
5 June 1858	Hon G.F. Hastings CB Captain
27 April 1863	H.E. Edgell CB Captain
20 June 1864	C.F.A. Shadwell CB Captain
25 January 1869	G. Wodehouse Captain

Inspectors General of Hospitals and Fleets

12 April 1869	J. Salmon MD
18 April 1873	W.R.E. Smart CB MD
13 November 1877	W.T. Domiville CB MD
25 November 1879	J.W. Reid MD
1 April 1880	D.L. Morgan CB MD
8 June 1883	A. Irwin CB MD

2 June 1884	J. Dick
7 June 1887	J. Breakey MD
25 April 1889	D.M. Shaw CB
2 January 1894	D. Hilston MD
2 January 1897	A. Turnbull MD
9 March 1898	H. McDonald CB
12 July 1899	H.D. Stanistreet
18 March 1901	R.W. Coppinger MD
15 March 1904	H.M. Ellis
1 July 1907	J. Porter CB MD
1 May 1908	T.D. Gimlette CB

Surgeons-General

1 May 1911	H. Todd CB KHS
5 June 1913	J.J. Dennis CB MD

Surgeon Rear Admirals

26 June 1916	C. Welch CB
4 October 1918	A.G. Wildey CB
5 May 1920	W. Bett CB MVO
26 April 1923	A. Maclean CB MB KHS
26 April 1926	D.W. Hewitt CB CMG MB FRCS
9 May 1929	H.C. Whiteside CB
7 May 1932	W.W. Keir CMG KHS
1 May 1935	C.L. Buckeridge CB OBE KHS
25 November 1937	T. Creaser MD BCh DTM&H KHP
25 November 1940	W. Bradbury CBE DSO MB BCh
27 January 1945	H.R.B. Hull CB KHS
27 October 1946	J.A. O'Flyn CB KHP
21 March 1948	J.A. Maxwell CB CVO CBE KHS
15 June 1949	F.G. Hunt CB CBE QHP
30 October 1952	J. Hamilton CB CBE QHS

30 June 1955	E.T. Rudd CB CBE QHS
30 June 1958	G. Phillips CB QHS
30 June 1961	D.D. Steel-Perkins CB CVO QHS
8 June 1963	J.M. Holford CB OBE FRCP
1 April 1966	E.B. Bradbury CB QHP
7 July 1969	N.S. Hepburn CB CBE QHS
30 June 1972	C.L.T. McClintock CB CBE QHS

Surgeon Captains

30 June 1975	A.P.M. Nicol MVO CBE FFARCS
4 May 1976	F.A.F. Mckenzie QHP FRCR
9 May 1978	P.W. Head OBE QHS FRCS
8 January 1982	J.W. Richardson OBE QHS FRCS
26 April 1983	J.B. Drinkwater QHS FRCS
3 April 1984	R. Radford QHS FFARCS
11 November 1986	D.A. Lammiman LVO FFARCS QHS
13 December 1988	F. St C. Golden OBE PhD MB Bch
4 September 1990	I.L. Jenkins QHS FRCS

Surgeon Commodore

1 December 1994	I.L. Jenkins QHS FRCS

Commanding Officers Royal Hospital Haslar

following Royal Hospital Haslar becoming a Tri-Service hospital on 1 April 1996.

2 April 1996	Brigadier G.E. Ratcliffe QHP FRCP
15 March 2000	Air Commodore T.W. Negus OBE FDSRCS

Commanding Officer Royal Hospital Haslar and Ministry of Defence Hospital Unit (MDHU) Portsmouth

following Royal Hospital Haslar entering into partnership with Portsmouth Hospitals NHS Trust.

30 March 2001	Surgeon Captain L.J. Jarvis MBBS FRCR
1 March 2003	Lt Col F. Tredgett RAMC
6 May 2003	Surgeon Captain L.J. Jarvis MBBS FRCR
9 December 2003	Surgeon Captain J. Campbell FRCS (Ed) FRCS (En)

On 31 March 2007, and following 253 years and 169 days of continuous service as a hospital, military command ceased.

Hospital Director

Haslar remained under MOD control until closure and a Hospital Director was appointed.

1 April 2007	Mrs Frances Allan BSc(Eng) Hons

Matrons Royal Hospital Haslar

Past Head Sisters and Matrons of RH Haslar

Head Sister

1885	Miss H. Stewart
1886	Miss B. Storey
1889	Miss L. Hogg
1901	Miss G.H. Mackay
1903	Miss F. Cadenham
1909	Miss E.E. Hart RRC
1912	Miss K.M. Hickey RRC
1922	Miss M.C. Clark RRC
1929	Miss C.C. Renwick RRC and Head Sister-in-Chief QARNNS 1934

Matron

1937	Miss D.W. Beale ARRC
1939	Miss M. Goodrich RRC
1944	Miss J. Gillanders RRC

Principal Matron

1946	Miss K. Baker RRC
1950	Miss G. Martin RRC
1953	Miss M.E. Gawston OBE RRC
1957	Miss K. Greenwood RRC
1959	Miss J. Woodgate RRC
1961	Miss S.K.E. Richards RRC
1962	Miss A.A.E. Burman RRC
1964	Miss A.I. Mitchell RRC
1967	Miss C. Thompson RRC
1970	Miss C. Cook RRC
1973	Miss P. Gould RRC

Matron

1975	Miss S.R.R. Barton ARRC

Matron

1976	Miss H.M. Scott ARRC
1978	Miss H.E.K. Gander ARRC
1979	Miss E.M. Northway ARRC
1980	Miss E. Wade ARRC
1982	Miss P. Greystone ARRC

Chief Nursing Officer

1986	Miss J. Titley ARRC
1988	Miss J. Massey ARRC
1989	Miss V.C. Fisher ARRC
1991	Miss C.M. Poole ARRC
1995	Miss J. Bancroft

Commander

1995	Commander J. Bancroft

Director of Nursing

following Royal Hospital Haslar becoming a Tri-Service hospital on 1 April 1996.

2 April 1996	Group Captain B.J. Forward ARRC PMRAFNS
9 March 1999	Colonel K. George RRC L/QARANC
9 October 2000	Commander E.M. Weall ARRC QARNNS

Senior Nursing Officer

following Royal Hospital Haslar entering into partnership with Portsmouth Hospitals NHS Trust.

30 March 2002	Commander E.M. Weall RRC QARNNS
15 September 2003	Commander N. Howes QARNNS

St Luke's Church Chaplains

Name	Date of Service
Mr Ritchie	1758-1763
Lewis Boisdaune	1763-1770
R. Hudson	1772-1797
J. Hall BA	1798-1812
Henry Lloyd DD	- 1813
David Evans	- 1813
Thomas Morgan	- 1815
A. Lawrence	- 1816
David Lloyd	- 1821
James Dunne MA	7 Jul 1828
William George Tucker MA	11 Mar 1853
George Jackson MA	7 Nov 1865
Robert Picton	18 Mar 1871
John James Harrison MA	15 Dec 1875
Frederick William Nickoll MA	27 Feb 1878
Bartholomew King LLD	3 Nov 1881
Alfred James Whistler BA	Mar 1884
George Mahon Sutton BA	Jul 1885
Charles Clark AKC	20 Aug 1885
James Payton BA	8 Apr 1887
Henry Barnett Harper BA	4 Sep 1890
Arthur Price Hill BA	18 Aug 1893
Octavius Rutherford Foster Hughes MA	7 Apr 1896
William Stuart Harris BA	12 Jul 1896
Charles Robert Mullins BA	6 Jun 1890

Hugh Keys Moore BA	1 Aug 1905
Henry Backwell MA	16 Sep 1908
Ralph Granby Sadier BA	12 Jan 1918
Thomas Wilfred L. Caspersz MA	15 Oct 1918
Christopher Graham BA	25 Nov 1920
Christopher Philip Godwin Rose BD MA	3 Sep 1925
John Archibald BA	1 Jan 1929
Noel Cyril Jones BA	27 Apr 1933
Vernon Kyrke MA	11 Aug 1933
Norman Braund Kent OBE MA	20 Sep 1936
John Wilfred Evans BA	28 Sep 1938
William Henry Stanley Chapman BA	1 Jul 1941
John Wiltshier MA	1 Feb 1944
Cyril Owen Amos Darby OBE	17 Jun 1946
Perry Malby Dodwell BD MA	24 Sep 1949
Charles Patrick de Candole	31 Jul 1953
Cuthbert Guy Desormeaux Long MA	9 Nov 1955
John Stanton Jeans AKC	1 Jan 1958
Julian James Andrew Newman BA	23 Sep 1960
Evelyn Hugh Jenoyr Levinge AKC	18 Oct 1964
Martin Kitchener Orme BD AKC	2 Mar 1967
David Vincent Evans MA	27 Jan 1970
Leslie John De Groose	17 Oct 1971
Peter Woodhall	9 Jan 1974
Anthony Arthur Upton	8 Mar 1976
Peter John Gregson BSc	13 May 1976
John Edmund Frank Rawlings AKC	3 Dec 1978
John Edward Goodband Clark	18 Jun 1981
Anthony John Francis Metters AKC	20 Aug 1982
Richard Francis Buckley	14 Jan 1985
Michael John Smith DipTh	23 Sep 1987
Stephen Philip Pickering SSC	23 May 1990
Steven David Brookes BA	20 Aug 1992
David Barlow QHC MA	4 Mar 1994
Christopher John Luckraft BA AKC	18 Feb 1997
Jeremy Peter Ames QHC BD AKC	27 Apr 2000
John Hill	12 Oct 2004

INDEX

Figures in **bold** refer to illustration page numbers.